FROM THE
EARTH
TO
MARS

FATH,
My Realm xxx

FROM THE
EARTH
TO
MARS

JEFFREY MANBER

The Surprising History

OF THE ROCKET PIONEERS
WHO LAUNCHED HUMANITY
INTO SPACE...

EPISODE

1

BEFORE
THE GOVERNMENTS
WERE INVOLVED

From the Earth to Mars

Published by Multiverse Media Inc
multiversepublishingllc.com
www.fromtheearthtomars.com
www.jeffreymanber.com

Conceived and written by Jeffrey Manber
Comics, pencil drawings by Jay Mazhar
Illustrations by Shraya Rajbhandary
Front Cover Image © Shutterstock
Front Cover and Book Design by *the*BookDesigners

Space Station V from *2001 A Space Odyssey:*
© NC Collections/Alamy

Starship Image: © Carter Goode

Paperback ISBN: 978-1-960119-67-4
eBook ISBN: 978-1-960119-68-1

Printed in the United States of America

TSIOLKOVSKY

LEY

LANG

VON HARBOU

REP

RYNIN

OBERTH

JAY
MAZHAR

CONTENTS

Introduction 1

EPISODE 1 **Germany Space Travel Pandemonium**

Verne's Influence... 7

Failed PhD Thesis.. 15

More Rocket Travel 21

The Silent Film...27

The Woman in the Moon................................... 31

The Impact...37

EPISODE 2 **The Russian Space Craze**

The Prophet of Space....................................... 41

Street Riots.. 47

The Russian Silver Screen................................ 49

On to Mars! 53

The Encyclopedia of Space............................... 57

Space Travel Exhibition 61

A True Space Businessperson............................ 67

Not in America!.. 73

Throwing Shade.. 77

Storm Clouds..79

Notes... 85

Bibliography 87

"'"Yes, gentlemen,' continued the orator, 'in spite of the opinions of certain narrow-minded people, who would shut up the human race upon this globe, as within some magic circle which it must never outstep, we shall one day travel to the moon, the planets, and the stars, with the same facility, rapidity, and certainty as we now make the voyage from Liverpool to New York!'"

Jules Verne,

FROM THE EARTH TO THE MOON
1865

"I WANT
TO DIE ON
MARS,
JUST NOT ON
IMPACT."

ELON MUSK,
SPACEX · 2013

Before the First Rockets,

BEFORE GOVERNMENTS
GOT INVOLVED

EPISODE

1

GERMANY'S SPACE
TRAVEL PANDEMONIUM
OF THE 1920S

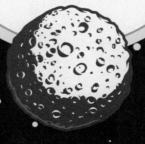

INTRODUCTION

On the morning of July 16, 1969, the crew of NASA's Apollo 11 blasted off on the journey that would—at long last—take humans to the surface of the Moon. Among the millions watching, none had done more to realize this epic journey than one Wernher Magnus Maximilian Freiherr von Braun, the first director of NASA's Marshall Space Flight Center in Huntsville, Alabama. The realization of humans at long last walking on the lunar surface launched von Braun into the rarefied atmosphere of celebrated American icon, one who reflected the can-do spirit of so many immigrant visionaries. But still, von Braun was not satisfied. At liftoff of the giant rocket, von Braun, watching from the Mission Control room, blurted out "give me $10 billion and I'll get a man to Mars."

The path that took von Braun to the Apollo 11 Mission Control room has often been hidden, ignored, celebrated or reviled. But it is the history of the rocket travel's journey in the 20th century and says much about the forces tugging at our exploration of space, never more so than today, as we seek to live and work not just on the Moon but on Mars as well.

•

Wernher von Braun was a visionary who eagerly worked with both John F. Kennedy and Adolf Hitler to implement his dreams of rocket travel. He was also a pragmatist who willingly developed the first wartime missiles because he understood the same technology could be used to take humanity into space.

Thus, the unholy alliance between the rocket pioneers and national governments was born. Von Braun was not alone. In Russia, Sergei Korolev and Valentin Glushko found themselves dealing with Stalin and later Soviet premier Nikita Khrushchev. So too the Chinese rocket/missile pioneer Qian Xuesen with both American and Chinese leaders.

American, Chinese and Russian leaders funded the development of the huge rockets of the nuclear age that also allowed space visionaries to develop civilian programs that fulfilled our timeless dreams of space travel.

Each side used the other.

Wernher von Braun Was a ...?

VON BRAUN WAS FETED AS A GENUINE AMERICAN HERO.

"(APOLLO 11) IS EQUAL TO THAT MOMENT IN EVOLUTION WHEN AQUATIC LIFE CAME CRAWLING UP ON THE LAND. THE MOON IS JUST A COMMUTER FLIGHT, GIVE ME $10 BILLION AND I'LL PUT A MAN ON MARS!"

JULY, 1969

NATIONAL BANK OF ALABAMA

NOVEMBER 16, 1963

A HERO WHO HAD HELPED CONVINCE JOHN F. KENNEDY THAT AMERICANS COULD BEAT THE SOVIETS TO THE MOON.

JANUARY 31, 1958,

THREE MONTHS AFTER THE SURPRISE SOVIET LAUNCH OF SPUTNIK, PRESIDENT EISENHOWER TURNED TO THE ARMY'S VON BRAUN TO LAUNCH AMERICA'S FIRST SATELLITE.

I DON'T TRUST THOSE GERMANS, BUT IF WE HAVE TO USE THEM, USE THEM.

1950s

I BELIEVE A PRACTICAL PASSENGER ROCKET COULD BE BUILT AND TESTED WITHIN 10 YEARS

VON BRAUN AND WALT DISNEY BRING SPACE EXPLORATION INTO AMERICA'S LIVING ROOMS. VON BRAUN HOSTED MULTIPLE TV SHOWS WITH WALT DISNEY WHICH MADE ROCKET TRAVEL EXCITING TO THE AMERICAN PUBLIC.

1955

A MANNED ORBITING STATION WOULD BE WONDERFUL AS A BOMBING PLATFORM.

1945

AS THE WAR WAS ENDING, VON BRAUN MADE SURE TO SURRENDER TO THE AMERICANS.

VON BRAUN WAS AN **AMERICAN** HERO WHO POPULARIZED SPACE TRAVEL, PLANNED THE APOLLO PROGRAM AND EMBODIED THE GRIT OF IMMIGRANT AMERICANS WHO MAKE A CHANGE FOR THE BETTER.

BUT MUCH OF THIS SPACE VISIONARY'S PAST *WAS HIDDEN* BY NASA AND SUCCESSIVE AMERICAN ADMINISTRATIONS.

VON BRAUN SHOCKED THE ARMY INTERROGATORS WITH TALES OF ROCKET TRAVEL.

ROCKET TRAVEL WILL CHANGE THE WORLD'S SCIENCE AND MILITARY SPHERES,

JUST LIKE AVIATION. SOON WE WILL EVEN BE ABLE TO GO TO THE MOON!

YOUR WONDER WEAPON COULD WIN THE WAR!

MAKE YOUR ROCKET WORK AND I'LL FUND THOUSANDS TO RAIN DOWN ON ENGLAND!

AS HE BECAME MORE IMPORTANT TO THE NAZI GOVERNMENT, VON BRAUN MET WITH HITLER ON MULTIPLE OCCASIONS. THE FUHRER BELIEVED VON BRAUN'S ROCKET COULD BE THE SECRET WEAPON TO HELP WIN THE WAR AGAINST THE ALLIES.

VON BRAUN
WAS A GERMAN
HERO

WHO DEVELOPED THE
MISSILES (THE FIRST ROCKET)
KNOWN AS
VERGELTUNGSWAFFE-ZWEI
OR "VENGEANCE WEAPON"
WHICH RAINED DOWN ON
BRITISH AND OTHER
EUROPEAN CIVILIANS.
THE NAZI GOVERNMENT
WANTED MISSILES.
VON BRAUN WANTED
SPACESHIPS.

OCTOBER 3RD, 1942
THE FIRST ROCKET IS LAUNCHED

TODAY WITH OUR FIRST SUCCESSFUL LAUNCH, MANKIND HAS REACHED OUTER SPACE!

1928
VON BRAUN JOINS THE GERMAN ROCKET SOCIETY

MY DREAM IS
TO DEVELOP
INTERPLANETARY
ROCKETS AND
PROFESSOR OBERTH
SHOWED ME THE WAY!
THE FUTURE WILL
BE SO WONDERFUL,
THERE IS SO MUCH
WE CAN DO WITH
SPACE TRAVEL!

AS A TEENAGER VON BRAUN WAS MENTORED BY THE ROCKET PIONEERS
HERMANN OBERTH AND RUDOLF NEBEL.

But at what price was this dependency on government funding for rocket travel?

The great innovations of the 20th century were all driven by entrepreneurs, whether for automobiles, trains or airplanes, or more recently, computers, the internet, biopharma or robotics. All these entrepreneurs worked closely with their governments, but the innovation was driven by the private sector. The result was efficiency in costs and agility in innovation, with governments as customers, not operators of the new technologies.

Why has rocket travel been treated differently—with a total reliance on public funding and the whims of politicians?

Even today space remains unique. NASA runs the American space program. There is the European Space Agency, Australian Space Agency, Russian Space Agency, UAE Space Agency. All technically advanced countries now have a space agency.

Why?

No industry has a dedicated government agency for a single market effort except for space. There is no internet agency, no automobile agency, no plane agency, no biopharmaceutical or robotics agency. Do we *really* need a space agency? Why?

Think about how different space travel would be today if rocket development had remained commercial like all other emerging industries. By now we would have colonies on the Moon and explorers on Mars. A dozen space stations would be manufacturing high-quality medicine and materials for use on Earth or serving as hotels for those seeking the ultimate journey.

Von Braun and many of the other pioneers took what was offered to realize the timeless dream to travel beyond Earth. By doing so, they abandoned their early idealism and helped make space exploration a uniquely governmental program from which we are only just emerging.

What should we do next? What is the right mix of government support for space exploration?

These are really important questions that will determine how we live and work on the Moon and on Mars. But these questions can only best be answered once we know the surprising story of how the rocket pioneers launched humanity into the space frontier.

Let's start at the beginning and let the story guide us far into the future. Episode 1 and 2 is the story of the beginning of space travel. That magical time in the 1920s when German and Russian visionaries brought engineers and mathematicians together with artists and investors and university dropouts to create the first communities of realistic space visionaries—which led to governments jumping into rocket travel

which lead to the development of **The First Rocket**

that led to space agencies being formed

that led to the race to the Moon

that led to the exploration exhaustion after America was first to the Moon

that led to today's vibrant return of entrepreneurs to space exploration.

•

So who did kick-start the serious interest in the exploration of space before the governments were involved? It must have been von Braun and his German team, right? Or an American? Or maybe a Russian? Was the first spark from an engineer or a farsighted politician?

Nope. Nope. Nope. Nope. How about a French writer!

DEFINITION: THE FIRST ROCKET

THE FIRST WORKING ROCKET WAS
LAUNCHED ON OCTOBER 3, 1942
FROM AN ISLAND OFF GERMANY
CALLED PEENEMUNDE IT TRAVELED
OVER 100 MILES AT A TOP SPEED OF
ALMOST 4,000 MPH. THE V-2 ROCKET
HAD AN APOGEE OF ALMOST 50 MILES.

THE FIRST ROCKET WAS A
BREAKTHROUGH IN ALL ASPECTS
OF NAVIGATION DESIGN AND
PROPULSION AND PAVED THE
WAY FOR INTERCONTINENTAL
BALLISTIC MISSILES (ICBMS)
PUTTING THE ENTIRE WORLD
UNDER NUCLEAR THREAT.

THE FIRST ROCKET WAS USED AS A
MISSLE ATTACKING LONDON AND
OTHER EUROPEAN CITIES. OVER 1,000
ROCKETS CRASHED INTO ENGLAND,
KILLING SEVERAL THOUSAND CIVILIANS

THE NASA APOLLO PROGRAM.
DEEP SPACE EXPLORATION.
COMMERCIAL SATELLITES. WERE
ALL MADE POSSIBLE BECAUSE
OF THE FIRST ROCKET. IN FACT
ALL LAUNCH VEHICLES TODAY,
WHETHER ELON MUSK'S FALCON
THE FRENCH ARIANE OR THE
RUSSIAN SOYUZ, AND THE
DOZENS OF NEW COMMERCIAL
ROCKET COMPANIES, OWE THEIR
EXISTENCE TO THE FIRST ROCKET!

CHAPTER ONE
It Was a French Novel that Inspired the Rocket Pioneers

1865

I f there is any one single event that set into motion the series of multinational events that began the true exploration of space, it was the publication of a book at the same time that the American Civil War was winding down.

In 1865 the French writer Jules Verne wrote *De la Terre à la Lune* (*From the Earth to the Moon*), the story of a three-man crew who are shot to the Moon by a long cannon built by the "Baltimore Gun Club."

Verne was known already for writing about extraordinary voyages like *Twenty Thousand Leagues Under the Sea* and *Journey to the Center of the Earth*. This time, he turned his attention to space travel and changed human-kind forever.

Others, of course, thought of space travel far before the French author. I mean, the ancient Chinese and Babylonians and Mongols had stories of humans leaving the earth and living in the heavens. The 17th-century Turks had a fable of a man flying to space using hundreds of pounds of gunpowder.

IN MY NEW BOOK I WAS INCREDIBLY ACCURATE IN SOME KEY AREAS: I HAVE THE FIRST MOON LAUNCH TAKING PLACE FROM THE COAST OF THE STATE OF FLORIDA IN AMERICA.

THE CREW ON MY ROCKET IS THREE PEOPLE AND ON THE JOURNEY TO THE MOON THE CREW EXPERIENCES WEIGHTLESSNESS, MEANING THEY ARE FLOATING BECAUSE OF THE LACK OF GRAVITY.

That was a brave explorer! And Hindu texts have flying spacecraft, translated as Vinmana aircraft, that could fly to the Moon and some say resemble the popular images of UFO's.

But in terms of the impact on the general population and, most importantly, the impact on the pioneers who would later write the first mathematical equations that paved the way for the first rockets, there is no question that Verne is the human who truly started us on the path to rocket travel.

How?

It is interesting, but not that important, that he nailed the launch location of humanity's first voyage to the Moon—Florida. I don't think anyone knows why he picked Florida. It is interesting, but also not that important, that the crew is a three-man crew, just like in the Apollo missions. Was NASA influenced by Jules Verne?

What is important about *From the Earth to the Moon* is that Jules Verne tried, really tried, to make the space voyage as technically accurate as possible for a time when no cars existed, no planes, no telephones.

The author did his own calculations to show that the idea of the cannon as a launcher would work. And that was new. The story stands in contrast to *The First Men in the Moon*, the H.G. Wells novel of 1901; that had his crew travel to the Moon via an antigravity machine. Kinda cool but kinda unrealistic.

There are three hugely important connections from young readers of Verne's book to the race to build the first rockets.

Romanian-German Hermann Oberth, who helped launch the German rocket effort and served as a mentor to Wernher von Braun, later swore that he had memorized the entire novel!

And Valentin Glushko, who designed many of the Russian rocket engines that took the first humans into space, admitted his love for *From the Earth to the Moon*. This means there is a direct link between the 1865 novel, **The First Rocket,** and the Russian launch vehicles—right up to the Soyuz launch vehicles that still, in 2022, are taking dozens of astronauts and space tourists to and from the International Space Station.

The "icing on the cake" in proving the influence of *From the Earth to the Moon* on today's space exploration is that one Russian reader did more than just be inspired by the novel. This reader sought to mathematically validate the use of Verne's long-range cannon to hurl humans into space. His name was Konstantin Tsiolkovsky.

The great Tsiolkovsky asked a practical question in the late 1800s before anyone else: would a cannon like the one shown in Jules Verne's book work to launch humans into space, or did you need something else, like a rocket? He asked the question as a scientist, as a mathematician, and not as a science fiction fan. As he explained, "probably (my) first seeds (on rocket travel) were sown by that author of fantasy, Jules Verne—he guided my thought along certain channels, then came a desire, and after that, the work of the mind."

Never heard of Konstantin Tsiolkovsky?

Tsiolkovsky was a partially deaf Russian schoolteacher who lived in Kaluga, a small town south of Moscow. He viewed living in space in religious

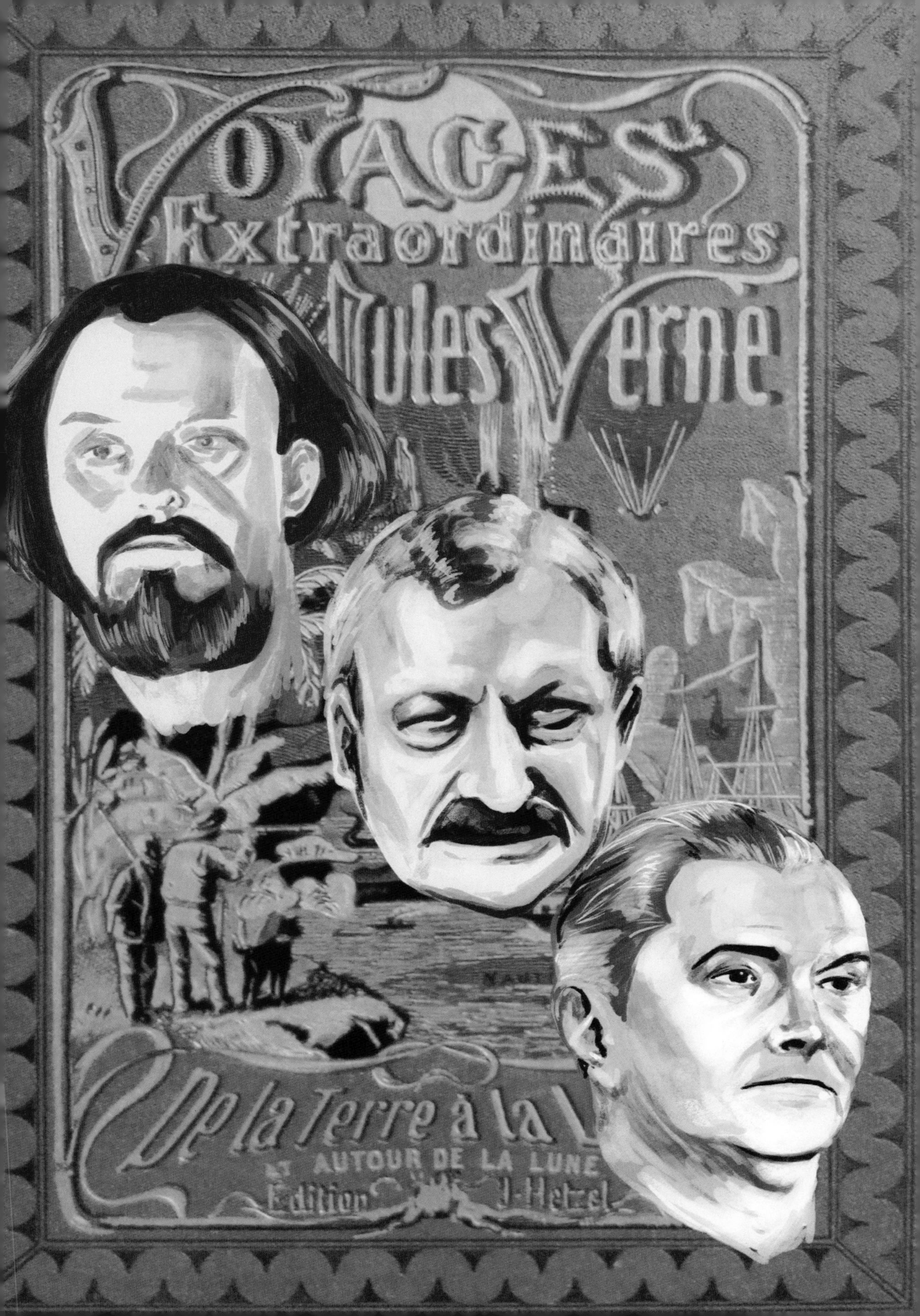

Voyages Extraordinaires
Jules Verne
De la Terre à la L
ET AUTOUR DE LA LUNE
Édition J. Hetzel

terms, believing that in space humans would find an immortal future.

But Tsiolkovsky was more than a philosopher. After reading Jules Verne's *From the Earth to the Moon*, this small-town schoolteacher set out to determine how realistic Verne's launch system was, before he finally calculated that shooting a projectile with humans beyond Earth's gravity would require a cannon of incredible length. What's more, the math showed that even if that was possible, the travelers would require a force so great that any crew member would be flattened like a pancake!

Leaving Jules Verne's cannon behind, he moved on to mathematically solve the challenge of rocket travel.

In 1897 Tsiolkovsky developed what we now call the **Tsiolkovsky rocket equation**, which predicted how a rocket would behave in the vacuum of space. Basically, Tsiolkovsky realized that a rocket burning fuel creates a thrust, or force, that would push the rocket in the other direction. This is a variation of Isaac Newton's second law that when unequal forces are acting on an object, the greater force pushes the object in the direction of the force. The famous F = ma (force equals the mass of an object times its acceleration). And acceleration is caused by unequal forces on an object. If the opposing forces were equal, the object wouldn't move!

All clear?

Well, this means that a rocket burning fuel will be pushed in the other direction, even in a vacuum. Many people in the 1800s, and even early 1900s, assumed that in the vacuum of space nothing man-made could apply the force to move forward. It was believed an atmosphere was needed.

The genius of Tsiolkovsky was that he mathematically predicted how a rocket could self-accelerate by applying thrust from throwing off its own mass. This is how one could escape the forces of Earth's gravity. Not via a cannonball like Jules Verne, nor by using propellers like the first airplanes that came along a decade after Tsiolkovsky's depiction of rocket travel.

Others later realized the same formula without knowing of the Russian school teacher, including the American Robert Goddard in 1912 and Hermann Oberth working in Germany in the 1920s. And a British mathematician developed the equation decades earlier. But Tsiolkovsky, for all his groundbreaking impact on rocket design and space travel, is given the honor of having the equation named after him.

His work was first fully published in the May 1903 edition of *Scientific Review* (*Nauchnoe Obozrenie.*) The thirty-page article, *Exploration of Space Using Reactive Devices*, detailed how a rocket would operate in space using a mixture of liquid oxygen and hydrogen, which is still among the most common launch vehicle fuels today. He then used his formula on the mass of the vehicle and the velocity to show a rocket could travel to space and in space.

Five years later, his most important stand-alone pamphlet was published: Исследование мировых пространств реактивными приборами

(*Exploration of Outer Space by Means of Rocket Devices*), in which he made the case that humans could journey from Earth into outer space and would do so via a rocket powered by certain fuels. In all, this extraordinary mathematical prophet of our future travels into space wrote dozens of books and pamphlets that predicted how we would develop rocket travel and live in outer space. Two others worth mentioning are the *Investigations of Outer Space by Rocket Devices* (1911) and *Aims of Astronauts* (1914).

This Russian reader of Jules Verne also predicted that a rocket ship, or "cosmic rocket train" as he sometimes wrote (how cool is that?), should be composed of three units or stages. The first would hold the crew, and the second and third the fuel, which he believed should be liquid hydrogen and oxygen. Abandoned was the centuries-old belief, starting with the Chinese, that small rocket projectiles were to be fueled by gunpowder. No, here Tsiolkovsky was aiming for a realistic, human-rated rocket, and needed was a fuel far more powerful than gunpowder.

You know? He was right! He was right about the fuel. He was right about the three stages.

So, did he become immediately famous?

Nope.

No one paid attention to Tsiolkovsky's work. Not at first—and so there he was, a teacher in the early 1900s, while at night formulating the basics of interplanetary space travel.

But the great space web had begun to be woven—a French science fiction book was written in the 1860s that inspired a schoolteacher in Kaluga, Russia to create the blueprint of the rocket by the early 1900s. How many stages the vehicle should have, the fuel, and how it would move itself through the vacuum of space.

And a German-Romanian reader of the novel later helped plant the seeds in Germany that directly led to **The First Rocket**. So too for the first launch vehicles in Russia that carried the first humans into space, that led to the great Space Race of the 20th century. That, at long last, inspired the commercial revolution of space exploration of the 21st century. Phew.

There were other early science fiction novels. The Polish writer Jerzy Żuławski wrote *The Lunar Trilogy* in 1901, about a crew that crash-lands on the Moon. Eventually the only survivor is a woman who gives birth, thereby launching a new lunar civilization.

The First Men in the Moon by the great H.G. Wells was a best seller, and yes, it did inspire Robert Goddard to start thinking about space travel, though it was published a full forty years after Jules Verne. But no matter, whether the British H.G. Wells or the French Jules Verne or other writers, we can say that these and other visionary books depicting an imaginary future of space travel, which later was known as science fiction, did pave the way for actual space travel.

Neil Armstrong Broadcasts from Columbia Module

"THIS IS THE COMMANDER OF APOLLO 11. A HUNDRED YEARS AGO, JULES VERNE WROTE A BOOK ABOUT A VOYAGE TO THE MOON. HIS SPACESHIP, COLUMBIA, TOOK OFF FROM FLORIDA AND LANDED IN THE PACIFIC OCEAN AFTER COMPLETING A TRIP TO THE MOON. IT SEEMS APPROPRIATE TO US TO SHARE WITH YOU SOME OF THE REFLECTIONS OF THE CREW AS THE MODERN DAY COLUMBIA COMPLETES ITS RENDEZVOUS WITH THE PLANET EARTH AND THE SAME PACIFIC OCEAN TOMORROW."

And just as amazing, Verne's novel remained front and center from the time of its 1865 publication to a hundred years later when humans finally landed on the lunar surface.

What do you think Jules Verne would have thought of Commander Neil Armstrong of the United States paying homage to his science fantasies while hurtling back from the lunar surface? We sort of know the answer. Verne's grandson Jean-Jacques Verne attended one of the first Apollo launches and told reporters that he remembered his grandfather saying he knew that one day his grandson would witness men actually blasting off for the Moon!

Let's keep the "Jules Verne Influence-Meter" moving forward, right up to the present: Who doesn't see the similarity between Verne's rocket and that of Elon Musk's Starship? Musk believes this is the launch vehicle that will take him to Mars. And NASA has awarded SpaceX a multibillion-dollar contract to have Starships be part of their current plans to have NASA astronauts (finally!) return to the Moon.

But there is more than the similarity between the rocket ship from *The Earth to the Moon* and that of SpaceX. In the science fiction novel, there is a strong rivalry between Florida and Texas as to who would have the launch site for the moon mission!

Included among the potential locations was southern Texas, now home to Elon Musk's Starship! Coincidence? Hey, Elon? Probably just plain good physics, though Verne had his rocket blast off from Tampa, Florida heading *west* instead of using Earth's rotation to maximize orbital efficiencies and launch *east*, as all rockets do today.

Let's do one more connection to show the respect today's space community has for Jules Verne. A visitor to Blue Origin, the Jeff Bezos space company, can sit in a really accurate model of the Verne rocket ship that dramatically rises up in their lobby. The interior of the rocket is a combination of a nautical ship with funky pre-industrial-age cockpit controls. Sitting inside, ~~all the while sipping space-branded whisky~~, makes real blasting off to the Moon in the 19th century.

Soooo, a direct connection exists between a novel written at the time of Abraham Lincoln to the WWII German developers of **The First Rocket**, to the rocket-design pioneers of Russia in the 1920s, to a shout-out from the crew of Apollo 11, to the Russian developers of the International Space Station cargo and crew vehicles, and right up to today's space entrepreneurs.

Verne and the visionaries of today share more than the design of the vehicles. All believe that rocket travel should be funded by the private sector, as much as by the government.

Verne's 1865 Moon Mission is owned and operated by the Baltimore Gun Club, a private organization. And the costs are paid for by subscribers worldwide, what we would call crowdfunding today!

Verne's narrator explains that:

> The sum required was far too great for any individual, or even any single State, to provide the requisite millions… despite of the matter being a purely American affair, to render it one of universal interest, and to request the financial co-operation of all peoples… The subscription opened at Baltimore extended properly to the whole world—Urbi et orbi.
>
> And the people respond, from Italy, Germany and France, all the way to Turkey. (England refuses at first, which uncannily mirrors their slow acceptance of human space travel!) And even Russian citizens support the Baltimore Gun Club mission:
>
> Russia paid in as her contingent the enormous sum of 368,733 'roubles.' No one need be surprised at this, who bears in mind the scientific taste of the Russians.

Verne predicted that rocket travel would be too expensive for companies, or even single nations, and that international support was critical. But his solution was not turning the mission over to the American government, but rather crowdsourcing for the necessary funds.

On all levels, therefore, Verne lit the fuse that blasted rocket travel into existence.

What was the next critical step that took humankind from the science fiction of *The Earth to the Moon* to **The First Rocket**?

CHAPTER 2
The Failed PhD Thesis
That Launched Rocket Travel
1922

Let's talk a little more about the inspiring story of Hermann Oberth. To a large degree, that humanity relies on satellites for instantaneous international communication and navigation, has seen the awe and beauty of the planet Earth from outer space, and has lived on orbiting space stations and traveled to the Moon is because in 1922 Hermann Oberth, the Romanian-German mathematician who was a fan of Jules Verne, had his quixotic PhD thesis *rejected* by the review board of the University of Heidelberg, Germany. A prestigious group of professors called Oberth's work too "utopian."

"OUR EDUCATIONAL SYSTEM, IS LIKE AN AUTOMOBILE WHICH HAS STRONG REAR LIGHTS, BRIGHTLY ILLUMINATING THE PAST."

Hermann Oberth

Hermann Oberth Defending his Thesis on Space Travel

BERLIN, 1922

I MAINTAIN THAT SOON *ROCKETS* WILL CARRY HUMANS FROM EARTH TO SPACE!

LARGE SILVER MIRRORS HOVERING IN SPACE WILL GENERATE FAVORABLE LIGHT FOR FARMERS IN WINTER!

THERE WILL BE MANNED SPACE STATIONS FROM WHICH SPECIALISTS WILL STUDY THE EARTH'S MORE REMOTE REGIONS.

THIS IS ALL POSSIBLE IN A FEW DECADES!

THANK YOU FOR YOUR CONSIDERATION OF MY THESIS. THIS WILL BE MY LIFE'S WORK AND THE WORK OF ALL HUMANITY.

AH-HEM. FRANKLY, WE CANNOT ACCEPT THIS AS A SCIENTIFIC WORK....

IT'S ALL JUST TOO..... UTOPIAN!

I'M NOT GIVING UP. I'LL PROVE TO YOU ROCKET TRAVEL WILL BE REAL IN OUR LIFETIMES!

AT TODAY'S STATE OF...TECHNOLOGY,
IT IS POSSIBLE TO BUILD MACHINES ABLE
TO ASCEND BEYOND THE LIMITS OF
EARTH'S ATMOSPHERE.

WITH ADDITIONAL REFINEMENT THESE MACHINES
WILL BE ABLE TO ATTAIN SUCH VELOCITIES THAT...
THEY WILL NOT FALL BACK TO EARTH'S SURFACE,
AND WILL EVEN BE ABLE TO LEAVE THE
GRAVITATIONAL FIELD OF EARTH.

THESE KIND OF MACHINES CAN BE BUILT IN
SUCH A WAY THAT PEOPLE CAN ASCEND WITHIN
THEM (PROBABLY WITHOUT HEALTH DISADVANTAGE).

UNDER CERTAIN ECONOMIC CONDITIONS
THE CONSTRUCTION OF SUCH MACHINES
MAY EVEN BE PROFITABLE. SUCH
CONDITIONS MIGHT ARISE WITHIN
A FEW DECADES.

After being turned down, the 29-year-old Oberth took the advice of his wife and published his rejected dissertation in 1923 as *Die Rakete zu den Planetenräumen* (*The Rocket into Planetary Space.*)

The self-published book was packed both with mathematical formulas proving that a rocket could travel in the vacuum of space and Oberth's ideas for space utilization, such as using space stations to monitor Earth's weather, fuel depots and launching spacecraft on to other planets.

Self-publishing his rejected PhD thesis was a courageous decision by Oberth, as the Germans value academic degrees as a necessary stamp of approval. By turning his back on the academic world, Oberth took a huge personal risk. Despite his publishing success, he was disappointed in Germany. "Our educational system," he said bitterly, "is like an automobile which has strong rear lights, brightly illuminating the past."

Here is the crazy part: Oberth's book was a surprise hit with a German public weary from their defeat in the World War. Here was an escape from the realities of the harsh everyday life of the economic depression. Who could have guessed a book with pages of equations would be a best seller? And a self-published book? That wasn't as common in the last century as it is today.

Hermann Oberth — Comments on Commercial Space

The genius of Hermann Oberth was that like Tsiolkovsky he moved beyond the equations. His book spoke of space mirrors and business models of in-space services. The book is raw—Oberth wrote of learning of Robert Goddard but passionately explained the evidence of how he had worked independently and prior to Goddard. Nonetheless, he praised the American for his work on a meteorite collusion equation and thinking to have flash powder ignite on a collision of a rocket on the lunar surface, so the impact would be visible from Earth. Oberth even wrote to Goddard, hoping to strike up a communication. But the first space race was on. Pioneers like Oberth were racing against competitors known (Dr. Goddard) and those unknown to build the first rockets and send the first humans into the frontier of space.

Oberth also assumed that in about thirty years, say about the 1950s, space travel would be a commercial and profitable undertaking. Like Jules Verne assumed. Like so many other pioneers assumed.

Elsewhere in the slim treatise Oberth admitted that *human* space transportation might not be economically viable, but "like electricity, new advances become so basic, one cannot predict with specificity the markets. but these markets will exist."

But the commercialization of space travel took far longer than Oberth or anyone imagined. He came to realize that governments had thwarted the dynamic progress necessary for commercial development of any new market.

How do I know he came to realize this? Because he told me in his caustic and dismissive style! I met Hermann Oberth when he was in the United States to witness the launch of a space shuttle. The space pioneer was the guest speaker at the Space Business Roundtables that brought Houston space engineers together with oil and gas investors, hoping to light a fire to launch non-government space activities.

Despite the commercial success of his book, Oberth found himself unable to land a professorship. The economic depression falling onto Germany did not help. Neither did the fact that this Romanian had been rejected by a respected university. Oberth left Germany and supported his family by teaching physics at the Stephan Ludwig Roth High School in Medias, Romania.

There is little doubt that this slim book, which sought to show that space travel was both physically possible and commercially doable, launched the critical first steps of rocket travel as both a cultural and technical craze that swept over Germany in the early 1920s.

Okay, let's move on.

MAX VALIER WAS TRAVELLING AROUND EUROPE SPEAKING ABOUT SPACE TRAVEL. HE WROTE SUGGESTING THAT WE FORM A CLUB TO RAISE MONEY TO FINANCE ROCKET DEVELOPMENT FOR OBERTH. LATER, WE HAD OVER 1,000 MEMBERS FROM DIFFERING COUNTRIES AND PUBLISHED A MONTHLY MAGAZINE.

CHAPTER 3
More Support for More Rocket Travel
1927

Sometime in 1927, a group of German space enthusiasts came together at the Golden Scepter, a popular beer hall in Breslau, Germany. The meeting was held to form the Verein für Raumschiffahrt "VfR," (Society for Space Travel). A society dedicated to space exploration!

One of the most influential of the organizers was a young man named Willy Ley. Ley was another outcast of German academia whose imprint on the public's perception of space travel would reach far, eventually into America's Apollo program of the 1960s.

Ley was a vocal admirer of not only Jules Verne but also the science fiction writer Kurd Lasswitz, who is referred to as the "German Jules Verne." Lasswitz published science fiction books with a scientific rigor far more advanced than Verne's. Not only was Ley a Lasswitz devotee, but so too a young Wernher von Braun.

Lasswitz's most influential book was the 1897 novel *Auf zwei Planeten* (*On Two Planets*), which has Earthlings meeting up with Martians from a far more advanced society. Everything from space stations to a Mars running out of water is depicted, as the aliens arrive at our North Pole to gather up the needed air and energy now lacking on their dying planet. Lasswitz was a century ahead in warning of the planetary concerns of climate change.

Like so many of the early space pioneers, Willy Ley had an uphill climb toward success. He had been forced to withdraw from university as the German economy began its horrific collapse in the years after their defeat in the World War.

But life for the university dropout dramatically changed when Ley came across Oberth and other rocket travel books in a Berlin bookstore. Not only was Ley smitten by the idea that space travel could become a reality, but the 20-year-old felt he could write a book more understandable to the general reader.

By 1926 Ley wrote the slim paperback *Die Fahrt ins Weltall* (*Jouney Into Space*), for which he received a large advance. The book sold as well as Oberth's, and Ley was on his way as a space expert.

At first the German authorities refused to grant the necessary license to the space club as "the aims of the association would not be apparent to the public, since the word 'space-travel' does not exist in the German language." Can you believe?

Finally, after much pushing by Valier and Ley and other devotees, the government authorities accepted that frontiers require a new vocabulary. Accepted by the German government were the stated aims of the society: "out of small projects large spacecraft can be developed which themselves can be ultimately developed by their pilots and sent to the stars." The first president was Johannes Winkler, a German designer who a few years later would launch a liquid-fueled rocket, though his efforts lacked a truly lasting consequence. Membership gained rapidly, in part via their magazine *Die Rakete*.

Max Valier was a driving force behind the first steps taken in Germany to develop a working rocket. His love of flying and for pushing the boundaries of the aviation frontier were obvious. Max was a veteran of the Austro-Hungarian Air Force, which had both observational balloons and a few dozen aircraft! But he wasn't an engineer. Valier was also a recognized journalist and, most importantly, had a knack for attracting the public's attention. Which was great for Germany's first steps in space exploration until, er, publicity wasn't so appreciated by the new folks footing the bills, as we shall see.

The VfR was international in its membership, as was true of any aviation or automobile society of the 1920s. The Russian Nikolai Rynin, who will be important to our story in later chapters, joined the society, as did one Hermann Noordung, which was a pseudonym for a Slovenian Austro-Hungarian officer in the Austrian Army named Hermann Potočnik, the author of the first dedicated book on space stations.

Let's talk about space stations.

The early pioneers focused on more than the rockets. They understood that orbiting space stations would also be important as humanity moved toward life on the Moon and Mars. What seems to be the first book published that focused heavily on space stations was published in 1929. Potočnik's book was called *Das Problem der Befahrung des Weltraums, Der Raketen-Motor. (The Problem of Space Travel: The Rocket Motor.)* Here's a random data point: his chosen pseudonym means "from the North" in German ("*norden*"). Why was this chosen for his literary career? Some believe Potočnik's selected name was an homage to Hermann Oberth, who came from the north, as had all the early German pioneers. Potočnik had joined VfR about two years before his book was published and was mentored, like so many other younger space pioneers, by Oberth.

The book was a sweeping examination of all aspects of the necessary space ecosystem. From rockets to space telescopes to space biology and, yes, the destinations. What is disappointing is that the commercial space station companies of 2022 are still working to implement many of the projects Noordung suggested in 1929, including on-orbit refueling and in-space manufacture.

The Problems of Space Travel influenced von Braun and other first-generation space dreamers. Von Braun cited the work in his PhD dissertation. Highlights of the book were even published in the American Science Wonder Stories, owned by Hugo Gernsback, a Luxembourger living in New York City who later developed the *Amazing Stories* pulp magazine devoted to science fiction and fact. Making this in-depth study of space stations the first German study translated into English for American readers. A few years later, it was also translated into Russian.

Noordung's work has been largely forgotten, in part because Willy Ley seems not to have liked Noordung and freaked out that Noordung placed his space stations not in what we refer to as low-Earth orbit, where all the space stations have been located, but in what we now call the geostationary orbit, which is roughly 22,000 miles from Earth. Oberth also criticized the writer on some very specific technical issues. And because Ley did not like Noordung, he never promoted his ideas like he unselfishly did for so many other pioneers.

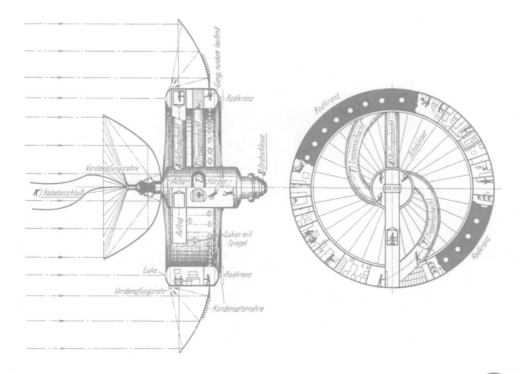

But Noordung's emphasis on the geostationary orbit was incredibly prophetic. Large satellites in the geostationary orbit are used today for sending television, internet and other data from one spot to another worldwide.

Few remember Noordung, not just because Ley refused to promote his ideas, but also because another visionary came along and became far more famous espousing many of the same ideas for use of the geostationary orbit. And this visionary was the popular science fiction writer Arthur C. Clarke.

Fifteen years after Noordung's book, Clarke wrote a magazine article that became famous for predicting the use of the geostationary orbit for international communications. Clarke's historic 1945 *Wireless World* magazine article was called: *Extra-Terrestrial Relays: Can Rocket Stations Give World-wide Radio Coverage*. In the article, he called for a network of three "rocket stations" that would provide global coverage for what today we would call a wired community.

Clarke later hit the big time with the 1968 Hollywood megahit *2001: A Space Odyssey*. The geostationary orbit is also known as the Clarke Belt, to honor the futuristic writer. All deserving, but when you dig into the details of his 1945 article, he sure got a lot of the architecture incorrect! Yes, he did: Clarke envisioned a group of three *human-occupied* space stations arranged in a triangle over 22,000 miles from the earth, launched by some version of the German V-2 rocket (**The First Rocket**) that would provide seamless radio communication around the globe. (One can well imagine that humans would have been in space far sooner if left to commercial interests. Had space companies existed in the 1940s, no doubt the first humans would have flown on variations of **The First Rocket**.)

And who did Clarke cite in the article? Well, none other than Hermann Noordung, who had earlier proposed geostationary "manned space stations."

And Space Station V from *2001: A Space Odyssey* rotated just like the station proposed by Noordung!

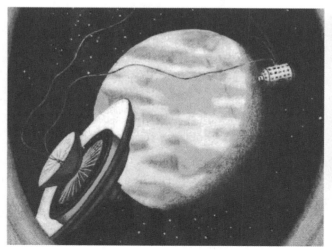

The rotating space station could well be known today as a Noordung station, and the orbit...well, Clarke was published in a popular American magazine that popularized the concept, so he got the naming rights to that orbit. For me, the distinction over and over as to who is important in the journey of space exploration is the influence of a given pioneer. Clarke had far more influence than Noordung, so he wins much of the credit.

But Arthur C. Clarke well understood that Ley should not have been treating Noordung so poorly. The famous visionary wrote in a letter to a colleague: "What an incredible man Potočnik must have been, perhaps in some ways quite as remarkable as Oberth."

So, the key question that must be asked: why didn't Hermann Potočnik-Noordung answer Ley's letters after publishing his groundbreaking book on space stations? Why didn't he correspond with Arthur C. Clarke? His silence infuriated Ley and caused this visionary to not receive the fame he deserved.

Um, because Noordung died on August 27, 1929, of a pulmonary disorder, soon after his *The Problem of Space Travel: The Rocket Motor* was published.

Upon learning of this fact *in the 1950s*, Ley was amazed: "no wonder he never answered anything, he died during the same year his book was published."

Yeah, Ley. Nice.

●

So, it was not just visions of space rockets that sprang from the VfR. The international membership influenced everything from satellite constellation concepts to human-rated space stations. There was even a group of members from South Africa, who later formed their own society.

Oberth, now respected as a best-selling author, became a member and acted as a mentor to the younger enthusiasts. Soon enough, a college kid started hanging around the club gatherings. His name was Wernher von Braun.

The VfR rocket enthusiasts were driven by pure romance, harboring plans of how space travel would soon take off like the aviation industry. Twenty percent of the members were engineers, the rest everyday people, from industrialists to pastors. As Willy Ley later remarked, the members wanted to spread the thought that the "planets were within the reach of humanity."

"To spread the thought" means to share with others, to take the best of rocket technology and discuss with other engineers, even those from other countries. And this could be done, before the governments got involved.

This photo is amazing for two reasons. First, it shows how quickly space travel would evolve in the next twenty years. Look how small that rocket is! But the photo is also extraordinary because it captures Hermann Oberth standing by the rocket while an eager young Wernher von Braun looks on from the right side.

Oberth must have enjoyed these first steps toward rocket travel. But it was not, let's admit, earth-shattering. A few volunteers created a space society. Some actually started to develop small rockets. Oberth must have been waiting for that breakthrough that would allow him to fully realize his dream of building an actual rocket. The offer finally did come.

But not from a university.

Not from a government official.

Not from a German company.

But from a movie producer!

CHAPTER 4
An Author and Famous Film Director Take the Next Steps to Space
1929

Someone very powerful in the German entertainment industry took notice of how the public ate up the space books and how local organizations like VfR were active in both experimenting with and preaching about space exploration.

That person was Thea von Harbou.

Here's what happened: Her husband was the famous Austrian film director Fritz Lang, who was enjoying a series of extraordinary successes, including *Dr. Mabuse the Gambler*, the fantasy film *Die Nibelungen* and most recently the science fiction classic *Metropolis*, which depicted a sparkling utopian city that is supported underneath by unseen mistreated workers. (What an impossible scenario!)

The director was eager to do something even more spectacular than Metropolis. What he had in mind was a realistic film based on a journey to the Moon.

His plan was something never done in science fiction history before or since. Via telegram (that's how long messages were sent before, well, before everything, even emails!), he invited the frustrated high school math teacher in Romania to serve as the film's scientific expert. Even more incredible, Lang had somehow convinced the German movie studio, Universum Film, better known as Ufa, to underwrite an actual launch tied to the film!

This was incredible since Ufa Studios and Fritz Lang had fought over the production of *Metropolis*, which was a critical success but with disappointing box office receipts. Given this recent experience, it was remarkable that the studio executives gave Lang another chance to exercise his creative ambitions, including the director's demand to exclude the use of the technical innovation known as the 'soundtrack.' It would be Lang's final silent movie.

Why did Fritz Lang want to do a movie about space travel? How did he know about Oberth? Well, it turns out that it was not the director but his wife who pushed for the project. The husband and wife were a famous team in the entertainment industry. Von Harbou had written a space-based thriller titled *Die Frau Im Mond* (*The Woman in the Moon*), and it was this novel that Lang successfully pitched to the studio owners.

THE IDEA FOR THE MOVIE IS MORE THAN
FOUR YEARS OLD. MY WIFE THEA, THOUGHT
ABOUT IT A LOT BEFORE WRITING THE NOVEL.
I HAD NO PART IN THE ARTISTIC DEVELOPMENT.
WHAT'S MORE, SHE STUDIED THE MOST
IMPORTANT PARTS OF SPACE TECHNOLOGIES
FOR YEARS. THIS IS REALLY HER EFFORT.

I LEARNED A LOT ABOUT SPACE TRAVEL FROM
HERMANN OBERTH AND THIS YOUNG MAN, A
UNIVERSITY DROP OUT, NAMED WILLY LEY.
I WAS VERY HONEST ABOUT THEIR
CONTRIBUTIONS, CREDITING BOTH
AUTHORS IN MY OWN NOVEL AND BRINGING
THEM INTO OUR FILM PROJECT.

Oberth, seeing how successful Willy Ley's own space book was, had expanded his first book to a 400-page epic volume titled *Wege zur Raumschiffahrt* (*Ways to Spaceflight*) and cleverly even dedicated the new book to Thea von Harbou and Fritz Lang, with his gratitude expressed first to Harbou.

In this larger book, Oberth explored new ideas, from how to ferry cargo to space stations to the use of what we now call orbital tugs, which are in-space vehicles that move between orbiting outposts. Orbital tugs do not quite exist yet, but I think we will have our first orbital tugs as the new era of private space stations come into reality. This visionary also explored industrial manufacturing to produce new materials in the zero-gravity of space, which is today also just being realized.

So without a doubt Thea von Harbou was inspired to author her own space travel novel by the books of Oberth and Ley and then pushed her husband to make his next movie about this new frontier. *Die Frau Im Mond* is still viewed today for its artistic merits and deserves equal prominence in the commercial space community as well.

Hermann Oberth Fleeing Berlin Absolutely Broke

WEST GERMANY, 1987

YOU SUFFERED FROM EXHAUSTION FILMING DIE FRAU IM MOND

AND RETURNED TO RUMANIA BEFORE THE FILM WAS FINISHED.

CAN YOU TELL US SOMETHING ABOUT HOW SICK AND EXHAUSTED YOU WERE

AND HOW LONG YOU NEEDED FOR YOUR CONVALESCENCE?

I WOULD NOT LIKE TO TALK ABOUT IT.

"OBERTH CAME TO BERLIN..AND FOUND HIMSELF IN... THE APPARENT TURMOIL OF A BIG CITY.... OBERTH BECAME GREATLY CONFUSED BY HIS SURROUNDINGS.... HE ARRIVED IN FOUL SPIRITS, STUBBORNLY REFUSING TO COMPROMISE ANY DEGREE OF SCIENTIFIC ACCURACY, EVEN PRIOR TO MEETING FRITZ LANG. OBERTH DISTRUSTED EVERYONE AND EVERYTHING AROUND HIM.... HE MISSED APPOINTMENTS BECAUSE OF HIS AFTERNOON NAP, TOLD THE TRUTH ABOUT IT, AND WAS LAUGHED AT HE ALSO VOICED HIS DISAPPROVAL OF BERLINERS, WHO "HAD NO SOUL AND WERE GERMAN-SPEAKING AMERICANS, HUNTING MONEY ALL THE TIME.... IT WAS THIS 'MYSTIC INCLINATION' THAT 'NATURALLY TRANSFORMED OBERTH INTO A NAZI IN DUE COURSE.'"

Willy Ley, 1944

CHAPTER 5
The Woman in the Moon

irst, the plot. This silent movie has it all: good guys, bad guys, a romantic interest, greed, dreams crushed and incredibly accurate depictions of rockets and interspace voyages from Earth to the Moon.

The main thrust of the plot involves an embittered veteran scientist who decades before was mocked for suggesting that the Moon's interior has larger deposits of gold than on Earth. An aviation businessman (the other frontier industry of the 1920s) agrees to fund an expedition to the Moon to claim the gold. A lunar gold rush is underway.

Soon enough, there are unscrupulous businessmen along for the ride (an American is the bad guy), wild struggles once on the Moon and a romantic drama-filled ending of two humans stranded, in love, on the lunar surface.

The accuracy of the fantasy lunar expedition shown on the big screen has stood the test of time. But wait, the director wanted more: a real rocket launch by the premier of the film!
The film's production schedule allowed only four months' time to build and launch one of the world's first rockets!

Oberth did not hesitate.

The professor assembled in Berlin the small community of men from across Europe who were already involved in space travel, principally from the VfR. These men included Willy Ley and Rudolph Nebel, a World War pilot also with little engineering experience. Nebel was recruited by Oberth via a newspaper ad looking for rocket experts and more than likely lied about his experience! Oberth came to regret his decisions during this mad rush and even decades later remained rueful about his work with Nebel. Oberth may well have felt that had he chosen the team better, the vehicle would have been ready for the film and the history of space exploration would be different.

While the film was being scripted and shot outside of Berlin, this ragtag group of dreamers and engineers feverishly struggled to bring to life the liquid-fueled Rocket Model E, one of the designs featured in Oberth's book *Die Rakete*.

Modifications were drafted, including an extra stage, but the core design remained. An engine design and even hardware was rapidly produced using local factories.

The result was a rocket, named for the main heroine in the film. Friede was about six feet tall and had a conical combustion chamber to mix the liquid oxygen and gasoline. Oberth theorized that liquid fuels would be far more efficient than solids. The inexperienced team experimented with gasoline being squirted into liquid oxygen. No gunpowder here, just as Tsiolkovsky predicted.

The plan between the movie people and the rocket team was to launch it over the Baltic Sea to an incredible height of 64 km, which would have been the first man-made object to enter the frontier of space. The 2021 suborbital commercial flight of Virgin Galactic, almost a hundred years later, reached 86 km, and the suborbital Blue Origin's New Shepard reached 106 km.

●

As might be expected, the four months proved a painful time. Events moved from bad to very bad. Delays piled on top of one another. And there seems to have been an accidental explosion which left Oberth temporarily blinded in one eye.

Ufa Studios stopped paying Oberth and the team, leaving him, as he said, "morally and economically bankrupt." Some say he suffered a nervous breakdown.

Finding himself in personal debt to the factory vendors who had been contracted for subcomponents for the Friede, Oberth skipped town. Imagine how it must have felt for Oberth, going from the incredible highs of just a few months before, back in Romania, to owing money to creditors.

But the filming continued, and the movie was able to include on the screen a rocket that sure looked like an early version of the NASA space shuttle!

And in a milestone event, on the evening of October 15, 1929, the film premiered to a capacity-filled crowd of over 2,000 attendees at the Ufa-Palast am Zoo cinema in Berlin—including one Hermann Oberth, who just couldn't stay away.

It was a spectacular evening. The façade of the theater was decked out to look like the star-filled universe. Spaceships flew out and back to a realistic-looking moon. Media attention was at a fever pitch. Not only was this the latest film of the great Fritz Lang, but Willy Ley had been paid to author a dozen articles on space travel to drum up publicity. Think of the opening night as the culmination of the Roaring Twenties. In just a few weeks, the Great Crash of Wall Street would collapse the financial markets and usher in the Great Depression.

There was a dedicated magazine for the opening night event, with articles by Lang, Oberth and others. Von Harbou was gushing in her depiction:

> This night turned out to be the most adventurous journey of my life so far: it became the optical vision of the journey to the Moon. Irrespective of what grew from the book into my cinematic brain, what I picked up or discarded, continued to ban or dropped: I was seized by the unique, irretrievable, irreplaceable delirium of enthusiasm for the subject matter.

Oberth? His usual dry self:

> The conquest of outer space is a very strange thing. In theory, we already know exactly how the journey will take place, how long it will take, what kind of machines we will need, how strong they have to be, based on which natural laws they have to work.
>
> Based on our current astronomical knowledge, we can state all this with the same certainty that we can predict a solar eclipse, for example. But that's not all. We already know how big and heavy such a spaceship has to be, we know that we cannot use the powder rockets that have been customary up to now for propulsion, but that we will only get further if we use liquid oxygen and some combustible substances (coal, gasoline, alcohol, hydrogen liquefied by cold , etc.) can burn together with the oxygen. A single rocket of this type would not yet reach a speed of 11.5 kilometers per second, but it will be necessary to stack several rockets one on top of the other, so that the lowest one always works and is ejected when its fuel is exhausted. Then their velocities add up, and in this way the desired final velocities are obtained.

What was shown on the screen was science fiction. But without a doubt Oberth contributed to the most realistic rocket and space scenes shown up to that time to the general public. And not just in Germany. Two years later, in 1931, the film made its debut in the United States.

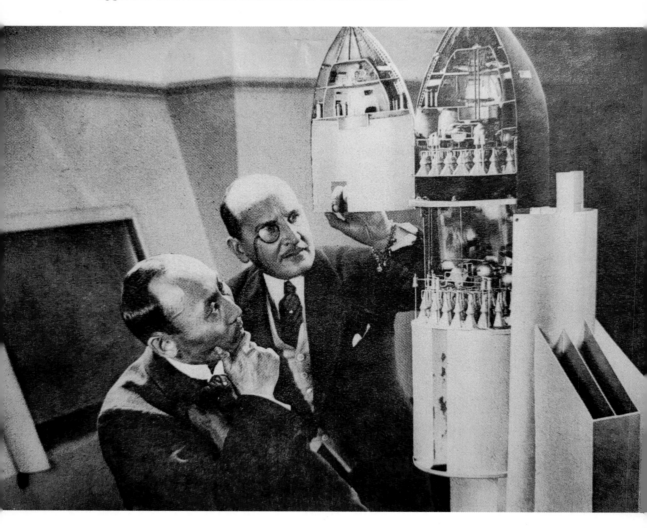

The Friede rocket had multiple stages, a liquid-fueled engine system and realistic calculations on escape velocity were displayed on the silver screen. Other cinema details that would prove prophetic included providing the crew with straps on the floor to hold them upright during the zero-gravity space voyage, and most consequently, the movie invented the dramatic countdown leading to a launch of a space vehicle. That's right, there is no engineering reason for a countdown. It was employed for dramatic effect!

The Invention of the Countdown

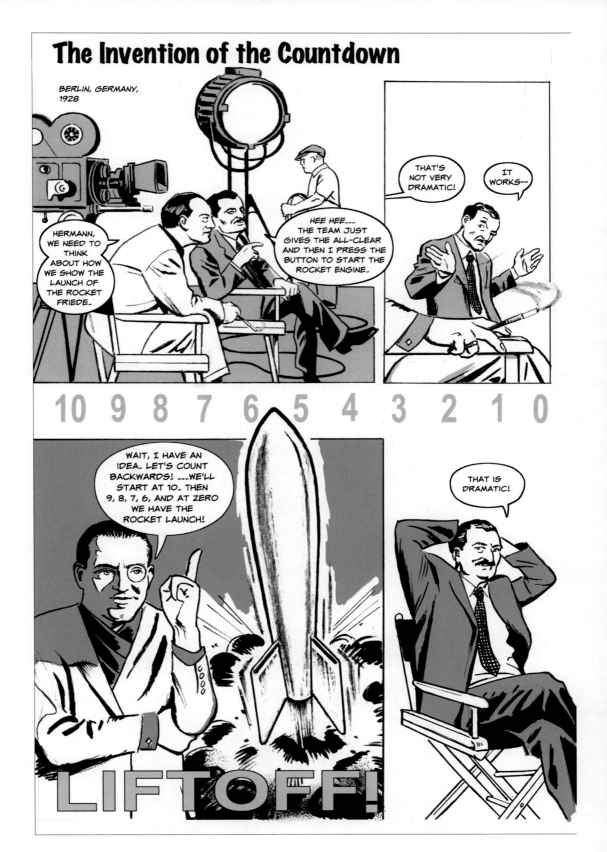

The plot also featured an uncrewed cargo vehicle (the H-32) that was sent first to prove the validity of the human-rated lunar program, yet another thoughtful Oberth innovation on screen that would later be employed in space exploration. Oberth understood the cost savings of an unmanned crew, and the safety considerations. You think using robotic cargo ships to lower the risk to astronauts is obvious? Well, NASA's space shuttle program used astronauts on missions that technology already allowed to be done without crew. It was the Russians who first embraced Oberth's concept, creating the dedicated robotic cargo ship *Progress* to fly to their space stations and later the ISS.

It is worth pointing out that yet again it was assumed, this time by von Harbou and Lang, that the future of lunar exploration would be undertaken for commercial purposes (lunar mineral extraction) funded by the private sector. Not for national prestige.

"ONE OF THE HIGHER ECHELON(S) FROM UFA WAS IN THE UNITED STATES AND HAD SEEN SOUND, HEARD SOUND—THE FIRST (AL) JOLSON FILM. HE ASKED ME TO MAKE SOUND WHEN THE ROCKET STARTS. AND FOR ME IT WAS WRONG. IT WAS BREAKING THE STYLE OF THE FILM, YOU KNOW? SO I SAID "NO." SO UFA SAID, "IF YOU DON'T DO IT WE BREAK OUR CONTRACT, WE DON'T PAY YOU ANYTHING." I SAID "OK, THEN WE WILL SEE... BUT I DIDN'T COLLAPSE."

Fritz Lang, 1972

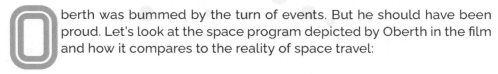

CHAPTER 6
The Impact of The Woman in the Moon

Oberth was bummed by the turn of events. But he should have been proud. Let's look at the space program depicted by Oberth in the film and how it compares to the reality of space travel:

—Unmanned vehicle looking a lot like **The First Rocket** (V-2)   yup
—Crewed vehicle looking a lot like the NASA shuttle   yup!
—Countdown methodology   yup
—Liquid-fueled engine   yup
—Sophisticated trajectory calculations   yup
—Unmanned vehicle as test for human mission   yup
—Straps to hold the crew during weightlessness   yup
—Retro-rockets fire to land the craft on the Moon   yup

And a harbinger of today's space companies:
—a commercial crew on a commercial mission   yup, yup!!

The film showed the far side of the Moon with plenty of oxygen, but that was done so the actors did not have to rumble around on screen in the suits they used when they landed, rather than Hermann Oberth believing there was oxygen on the lunar far side!

One other intriguing detail. The rocket in the movie was named Friede, for the heroine. But Friede is also German for "peace." Decades later, the Russian space station was named Mir, which is Russian for…"peace"! A coincidence?

●

So, a great story all-around. One of the most famous directors of the time produces a film on the new space frontier. And the idea came from his wife, who was a respected author and cultural figure. A modern-styled husband and wife team. Great, right?

Well, there is one dark side to this story. Von Harbou was a proud member of the German Nazi Party. There is speculation that the reason for her novel, the reason for her wanting her husband to not only produce a space-based movie but also an actual rocket with Hermann Oberth, was to capture the attention of Nazi Party leaders for using rockets as offensive weapons.

Remember, this was in that period when many in Germany were smarting over not only their loss in the World War, but their perceived poor treatment by the Brits and French, which barred Germans from building up military capabilities. But "missiles" were not on the banned list, a point known to the German rocketeers and, soon enough, to German authorities.

We don't know for sure if this was the reason for her interest in space travel. But maybe, just maybe, it was because of von Harbou and her husband's film that the German government began watching and eventually supporting the VfR and the amateur rocket enthusiasts.

●

By the end of the 1920s a tipping point had been reached in Germany. There was no going back. **The First Rocket** was soooo close. The rocket parts built but never used for the film were grabbed by the VfR engineers. There was strong public support and German industry was engaged. All in a few short years. Space travel seemed inevitable.

●

Germany, by 1929, had best-selling books on rocket travel, a space society filled with idealistic engineers, a blockbuster silent film based on lunar exploration, several commercial programs to build rockets, all bubbling to a critical mass to make space exploration a commercial business.

Question: Is there a chance that these same ingredients came together in another country? If so, what country?

Answer: Yes. Amazingly, another country went through the same public fascination with space travel in the 1920s. And it was not America. It was Russia!

Let's go find out what the Russian space exploration craze of the 1920s looked like and how it too played a role in creating humanity's push into the space frontier. And how each country's visionaries propelled each other further along in the race toward **The First Rocket**.

EPISODE

2

THE
RUSSIAN
SPACE
CRAZE

I BELIEVE IN THE SCIENTIFIC RELIGION OF COSMISM AS
TAUGHT BY NIKOLAI FYODOROVICH FYODOROV.
HOW LUCKY I MET NIKOLAI FYODOROVICH
WHEN I WAS A TEENAGER! HIS COSMISM SHOWS
US THAT VIA SETTLEMENTS ON OTHER PLANETS
HUMANITY WILL ACHIEVE IMMORTALITY!
BECAUSE OF NIKOLAI I UNDERSTAND THAT
THE EARTH IS THE CRADLE OF HUMANITY.
BUT MANKIND CANNOT STAY IN THE CRADLE.
OUR POPULATION IS GETTING BIGGER AND IT
WILL NOT END. I UNDERSTAND THAT LANGUAGE
IS THE MEANS TO COMMUNICATE NOT ONLY WITH
THE LIVING BUT ALSO WITH THOSE WHO HAVE
DIED BEFORE US. AND THAT WE CANNOT ACHIEVE
IMMORTALITY WITHOUT ALSO RESURRECTING THOSE
SOULS THAT HAVE DIED BEFORE US. VIA OUR CONQUEST
OF SPACE AND A GREATER UNDERSTANDING OF SCIENCE
THE HUMAN SPIRIT WILL ACHIEVE ITS FULL POTENTIAL I
BELIEVE SOME TIME IN THE FAR FUTURE WE WILL REACH
A STATE OF "COSMIC OPTIMISM" AND IMMORTALITY WILL
BE PART OF THE HUMAN RACE. I AM PROUD OF
THIS RUSSIAN BELIEF.

CHAPTER 7
The Prophet of Space
1923

We started our history of space travel in Germany because there is a direct line between the early German space community and **The First Rocket**. But in one of those strange quirks of history, Russia was experiencing the same fever-pitched excitement for space travel as Germany. And both countries had many of the same ingredients that contributed to the advancement of humankind's most spectacular dreams of travel.

If Jules Verne was the popular instigator of rocket travel, there was one man who over time was realized to be the spiritual founder of space travel.

We met him earlier, and he is, of course, Konstantin Tsiolkovsky. Though there are many pioneers of our exploration of the space frontier, including those who designed the first rockets and space stations, dreamed of lunar colonies, developed sophisticated plans to make money or move humanity

KONSTANTIN EDUARDOVICH EXPLAINS MY COSMISM VERY WELL! THE QUESTION OF THE FATE OF THE EARTH LEADS US TO THE CONVICTION THAT HUMAN ACTIVITY MUST NOT BE BOUND BY THE LIMITS OF THE EARTHLY PLANET. THE CREATOR RE-CREATES THE WORLD THROUGH US. AND THEREFORE MANKIND MUST NOT BE AN IDLE PASSENGER, BUT THE CREW OF OUR EARTHLY SHIP, SET IN MOTION BY A FORCE AS YET UNKNOWN.

into the frontier, it all comes back to Konstantin's extraordinary probing of rocket travel at the start of the 20th century, two decades before the Russian and German renaissance in space efforts.

What drove Konstantin Tsiolkovsky to dream of space and spend hours after his school job creating the mathematical models that proved rockets could travel through the vacuum of space? It might help to understand that Tsiolkovsky took his inspiration from a mysterious Russian philosopher who believed that in the frontier of space humans would find a utopia. This belief is called cosmism.

Nikolai Fyodorov's belief that the immortality of the human race would be realized in outer space has influenced many, including the famous Fyodor Dostoevsky (he wrote some of the greatest Russian novels, including in 1866, *Crime and Punishment*) and several generations of modern painters and philosophers. The Russian excitement toward space was in part based on Fyodorov's philosophical utopian underpinning. His cosmism is like a secret religion that still, even today, is respected by Russian space engineers.

But cosmism is alive today not only among the Russian space community but in current philosophies that blend spirituality with technology. An example might be transhumanism, which seeks to blur together technology and the human body, to create post-humans with greater happiness and longevity. One of the first adherents was a philosopher who changed his name to FM-2030.

Cosmism's continued influence is even more unusual given that Fyodorov did not believe one should write articles or books, and he apparently wrote none.

Before we leave cosmism there is something curious to mention about Nikolai Fyodorov. This founder of the most influential philosophy based on space colonization was born out of wedlock in 1828 or 1829 to a Russian prince named Pavel Ivanovich Gagarin.

Let's jump more than a hundred years into the future. April of 1961, to be exact. Sergei Korolev, the head of the secretive Russian space program, has a choice: who should he anoint to be the first human to travel into outer space? There are two outstanding candidates: Gherman Titov or Yuri Gagarin. Who does the superstitious Korolev pick? The man named Gagarin. The man whose family name is the same as the spiritual philosopher of the Russian journey into space. Coincidence?

●

No matter his powerful impact on future generations, October 1923 was a bad time for the slightly deaf schoolteacher. A few months earlier his son had committed suicide, just a year after his daughter had died from tuberculosis. Earlier, a flood almost destroyed his house and with it his collection of his scientific writings.

What's more, the newly born Soviet Union was reeling from the Revolution that brought on a brutal Civil War. Vladimir Lenin and the communists had overthrown the czar. Nothing was certain in Russian society.

Tsiolkovsky had even been arrested and briefly jailed by the secret police on trumped-up charges of treason.

Compared to his personal travails, the German university's refusal at about the same time to approve Hermann Oberth's PhD doctorate thesis on space exploration seems less draconian.

So, not the best time to have one's life work ignored in an article on space travel by Russia's largest newspaper.

But the futuristic mathematician toiling in the small Russian town of Kaluga must have been used to being ignored. He had spent two decades working on his concept of metal dirigibles with little government support, even while French and German aviators like Charles Renard and Ferdinand von Zeppelin were thrilling the public with lighter-than-air ships.

Tsiolkovsky's studies on space travel was suffering from the same fate as the dirigibles. His incredible 1903 article and later pamphlet on "rocket trains" mathematically examined the principals of interplanetary flight. And Tsiolkovsky was the first to advocate the use of liquid fuel as rocket propellants. Yet few took notice.

But sometimes being slighted turns out for the best. Sometimes. And luckily, this was one of those times. The 1923 newspaper article that so angered Tsiolkovsky and kicked the emerging space community into an entire new level of international coordination was on page four in the leading Russian newspaper *Izvestia*, entitled *News of Science and Technology*.

The reporter waxed with enthusiasm about the German-Romanian Hermann Oberth and his just-published book on rocket travel, *The Rocket into Interplanetary Space*, which proved for the first time, wrote the reporter, that space travel was possible!

To put a healthy overdose of salt into the wound, the reporter also noted that Oberth's work provided the mathematical foundation for the American Robert Goddard and his efforts to build a moon rocket!

No mention of Konstantin Tsiolkovsky. Dissed in his home court.

The response from the small group of scientists who knew of Tsiolkovsky and his published articles was swift and filled with outrage. Today, we would say the article went viral.

Defenders wrote to *Izvestia*, which published a three-page rebuttal, far longer than the original article. And colleagues also put forward stout defenses in scientific magazines explaining how Russia had its own theoretical mathematician and space visionary, just like in Germany and America. Sometimes it's easy to forget a farsighted visionary—that is, until your country's honor is at stake!

And Tsiolkovsky swiftly counterattacked by republishing his original 1903 material. Smart move.

A long-distance mutual respect blossomed between the two pioneers, in some ways helped by a Russian space writer and émigré to Germany named Aleksandr Scherschevsky

Aleksandr Scherschevsky's role in space history is assured in that he was instrumental in helping foster the mutual respect between these two great rocket pioneers. But his own personal reputation was a little—well, Hermann Oberth didn't exactly leave a glowing recommendation. Scherschevsky, said Oberth, was "an emigrant who lived completely in filth. I had the feeling that if one threw him against a wall he would stick."

Not the best compliment.

Fortunately, Scherschevsky "stuck" to Tsiolkovsky, calling him the "prophet of interplanetary communications." (That is how space travel was often referred to in 1920s Russia.)

Ley ganged up on Scherschevsky as well. Just like with Noordung, Oberth and Ley were a powerful tag team to beat up on fellow pioneers not trusted or respected. Ley was angry about a recounting in Scherschevsky's book *Die Rakete für Fahrt und Flug* (*The Rocket for Travel and Flight*), in which he has the Russian czar supposedly meeting with both Tsiolkovsky and the French space businessman Robert Esnault-Pelterie. "He could have done better," dryly opined Ley, "if he had written about Russia, but he didn't." Ouch.

Scherschevsky regularly wrote to Tsiolkovsky, telling him of the German space efforts, the progress of the American Robert Goddard, and probably most enjoyable to Tsiolkovsky, his own growing importance in Germany. More than likely, he gave Tsiolkovsky's republished pamphlet to Hermann Oberth to read.

But he was not the only German letter writer to the Russian pioneer. Willy Ley also corresponded, as did other German rocket scientists. From Germany, there was a growing respect, almost amazement, at this visionary Russian pioneer, accomplishing so much outside of formal academia and industry, and years before those in the rest of Europe.

It is impossible to know whether the Russians public's fascination with space travel erupted due to the outrage from this *Izvestia* article—but there is no doubt that a groundswell of enthusiasm in Russia toward rockets and their own pioneers in this new frontier erupted in the months and years afterward. Like in Germany, "interplanetary communications" was now a hot fad, bringing together artists and writers with mathematicians and a public that could not get enough of space travel.

Konstantin Tsiolkovsky Is Rightly Indignant

KALUGA, RUSSIA, 1923

CHAPTER 8
Fake Space News Stirs Street Riots
1924

How popular was space exploration after the *Izvestia* outrage? Well, some newspaper reporting led to a riot!

In the spring of 1924, rumors swept through Russia that the American professor Robert Goddard was ready to send a rocket to the Moon! The rumor bubbled into Russian society, causing interest, consternation, wonder and so many questions that no one could answer.

Was this for real?

In order to find out what was happening and share the news with the public, students at the Zhukovsky Engineering Academy in Moscow formed the "Society for the Study of Interplanetary Communications." This is believed to be the world's first rocket society, as it was a couple of years before the German VfR. The eager group of students sponsored discussions with noted university professors and with the Russian media, fanning further the flames of space travel interest. Involved in the formation and guiding the organization was none other than Friedrich Tsander.

And you see the irony? The world's first rocket society was energized… in the Soviet Union because of…the American rocket designer Robert Goddard! How crazy is that? This is the first example of the famous "Superpower Rivalry" in space, but this incident was far healthier. And the heartfelt reaction showed the genuine Russian enthusiasm for space travel. It was, sadly for Goddard, a one-way enthusiasm as, like Tsiolkovsky two decades earlier, Goddard was pretty unknown in his own country.

Speculation about the American mission to the Moon continued from spring into the summer of 1924.

The noted Russian space visionary Yakov Perelman (also a member of the German VfR society) wrote what we would now call a "fake news" piece in the newspaper the *Late News*. Perelman confidently informed his readers that a rocket to the Moon would launch on the American July 4th holiday. Wow!

But, sorry. Nothing happened in July. No launch. Goddard had a whole heap of technical challenges and funding troubles, and there was zero chance Goddard was launching a rocket to the Moon.

By summer's end, as confusion mounted in Russia over the absence of an American launch to the Moon, the student society organized an event in a large auditorium at the Physical Institute of the First University. The result was beyond anyone's imagination: there was pandemonium, crowds had to be contained by the horse militia, and it required not one but three October evenings of debating to satisfy the public's thirst. Even the *New York Times* got involved, printing a letter first from a 'gentleman' and then a 'young lady' stating they were ready to fly to the Moon on Goddard's rocket. (The man asked for $10,000 in insurance.)

Imagine…police on horses to handle a mob of…space enthusiasts! The convoluted affair may have led to the closing of the rocket society by the end of the year.

In the meantime, some Russians took the issue into their own hands and wrote directly to Robert Goddard. And guess what? Goddard answered several of the letters and even sent copies of his few published articles. From these articles, one could easily understand that no Goddard rocket was soon to launch to the Moon.

It is fair to say, is it not? That no doubt the American space visionary was far more popular and far more influential in Russia and Germany than in his own country.

Think about that.

The Russian public wanted more on space travel. The visionaries were happy to oblige.

So too were Russian artists.

"FUTURE HISTORIANS WILL REMEMBER 1924 AS THE DATE FOR ONE OF THE GREATEST STAGES IN THE EVOLUTION OF TECHNOLOGY … 4 JULY OF THE PRESENT YEAR HAS BEEN NAMED AS THE DATE FOR SENDING THE FIRST PROJECTILE TO THE MOON … PROFESSOR GODDARD … HAS NAMED THAT DAY WHEN THE FIRST GIGANTIC ROCKET WILL CAREEN INTO THE MOON."

Yakov Perelman

CHAPTER 9
To Mars on the Russian Silver Screen
1924

The Russians had their own blockbuster silent film on space travel, just like *The Woman in the Moon*. And again, like the world's first space society, the Russian space movie was first, before the German space classic.

The movie was *Aelita: Queen of Mars*. The film premiered in 1924, four years before Lang's classic. The director was Yakov Alexandrovich Protazanov.

Aelita is the dark story of an interplanetary romance between a Russian engineer and a beautiful Martian princess. It was based on a 1923 novel by Alexei Tolstoy, a distant relative of the great Russian writer Leo Tolstoy.

The main character is a Moscow engineer named Los, who has visions about a woman named Aelita. She is the daughter of a repressive government leader on Mars. Aelita has seen Los through a telescope and falls in love with him. (Kinda creepy, no?)

In his fantasies, Los seeks to help Aelita lead a worker's revolt against the Mars Elders and create a Martian socialist republic. To support the workers' uprising, Los designs and launches an egg-shaped ship and travels to Mars.

The film was an immense hit, helped along by a teasing pre-opening campaign in *Pravda* and other major Russian newspapers asking, "What is the meaning of mysterious signals received by radio stations around the world? Find out on September 30th!"

The movie studio even paid for leaflets to be dropped from airplanes circling over Moscow. That in and of itself was a novel use of airplanes in 1924.

Opening night saw packed crowds eager to get into the theater. Inside, there was a live orchestra performing music commissioned just for the event. At some later performances, the legendary pianist Dmitri Shostakovich played the movie score.

The best barometer of how the story touched a cultural nerve with the Russian people is that "Aelita" became a very popular name for Russian newborns! Of course, the film was not as technically accurate as Lang's *Woman on the Moon*. The movie had no Russian equivalent to Hermann Oberth. Nor did the studio fund a group of space experts to launch an actual rocket. And even in the film itself there were no technical details introduced on the screen.

In that sense, *Aelita: Queen of Mars* is much like H.G. Wells's *First Men in the Moon*. Influential, but not technically meaningful.

Unfortunately, Russia's new political leaders took a dislike to the space film. In the post-revolutionary Soviet Union there was suspicion toward the "elites" living in the cities, as well as any project that was backed by internationalists. The political loyalties of the director Protazanov and the writer Tolstoy were under suspicion, as both men had fled to Europe after the Russian Revolution. The director was also a believer in Fyodorov's cosmism. That was a big no-no to the Soviets, who wanted communism to be the people's religion.

Also of concern to the Soviet leadership was how the movie's costume designer hung out with avant-garde European artists like the painter Pueblo Picasso. This was all too much. A push back against the film was launched. One critic wrote: "The much-talked-about *Aelita* was received by worker audiences in the provinces with considerable doubt as to its usefulness." Oh. Not good.

More political criticism followed. *Aelita* was criticized by the Soviet Writers Union for being made mostly for Western audiences. Another, equally dangerous attack stated that the film was focused more on technology's impact on the future—which was the role of the new Soviet leaders. Um, yeah, that's what science fiction is, right?

Soon enough, the movie was withdrawn from the public. It's a small point in space exploration history, that a popular film featuring a love story on the planet Mars was pulled from being shown in the post-revolutionary Soviet Union. But perhaps it was another, less enviable first in the exploration of outer space: the first time that politicians began censoring space-related material, no matter the public enthusiasm.

Though the movie is largely forgotten today, film experts believe the focus on futuristic rockets and alien landscapes as scenes for a popular film might have influenced Thea von Harbou and her interest in space travel a few years later.

Russia's *Aelita: Queen of Mars* may have unwittingly helped popularize the German space effort that later pushed forward the construction of **The First Rocket**!

"THOUSANDS GATHER AROUND LOS'S WORKSHOP IN ANTICIPATION OF THE BLASTOFF. GOVERNMENT OFFICIALS COME, AND SPEECHES ARE MADE. FINALLY, GUSEV AND LOS... GET INTO THE EGG-SHAPED SPACECRAFT. BEFORE CLOSING THE HATCH, LOS TELLS THE CROWD, "I'M CERTAIN THAT IN A FEW YEARS HUNDREDS OF SPACESHIPS WILL PLY THE COSMOS. WE SHALL ALWAYS--ALWAYS BE DRIVEN BY THE SPIRIT OF QUEST." SOMEWHAT ENIGMATICALLY, LOS CONTINUES, "I'M NOT A GENIUS, NOT A BRAVE MAN, NOT A DREAMER. I'M A COWARD—A FUGITIVE."

AELITA, the novel by Alexei Tolstoy

CHAPTER 10
On to Mars, On to Mars!

O ne other Russian space visionary so important in the 1920s needs to be introduced. Remember the *Izvestia* reporter who forgot about Tsiolkovsky? The reporter had the good sense to remain anonymous, so we don't know who he/she was. The journalist also ignored the high-energy, incredibly admired Friedrich Arturovich Tsander, who paved the way for the next generation of Russian space designers.

Throughout his brief life (he died at 45), Friedrich Tsander had one goal and one goal alone: to travel to Mars!

Born in Riga, Latvia in 1887, Tsander at every age sought to involve every-day people in his quest to realize a mission to the Red Planet. He first read Tsiolkovsky's pamphlets in Riga High School and never looked back. He wrote to Tsiolkovsky, starting a multiyear correspondence between the elder vision-ary and the young man. How could a teenager living in the early 1900s, before there were rockets, have a passion, a true passion, about going to Mars? That is the definition of a true believer in space travel.

No, wait, I have another definition of a true space believer: he later named his daughter Astra (Latin for "the stars") and his son Merkuri for the planet.

As a university student at Riga Polytechnic Institute, Tsander successfully petitioned the facility to establish a student-run society devoted to interplan-etary flight. He was later involved in Leningrad when the student rocket soci-ety was put together. Tsander was admired by both Tsiolkovsky and one of the leading Russian writers on space travel, Nikolai Rynin, because of his nev-er-ending evangelizing about the new frontier. Tsander was constantly on the move, visiting even the smallest towns in Russia promoting the space frontier to whoever would listen. Imagine, in some Russian village of the 1920s, fresh from the bloody Civil War, listening to this Latvian waxing about the beauty of rocket travel and the immortal life possible by living among the stars. It had to have been a powerful elixir.

Tsiolkovsky did his part with Tsander by publishing people's names and addresses in the back pages of his pamphlets to help create a space-en-thusiast network. In this way, the space-obsessed public could contact one another and create a community.

A colleague wrote that "in 1914 Tsander was the first engineer in our country to devote himself to the practical solution of problems connected with interplan-etary flight and rocket technology. 'Flight to Mars' was his slogan throughout life."

Another contemporary described well Tsander's role among the rocket pioneers of the 1920s: "K.E. Tsiolkovskii was the first scientist…to point that rockets were the only possible means of reaching outer space…and reaching velocities of over 11 km/sec…However he provided no engineering solutions to the problems of the rocket…Foreign scientists Esnault-Pelterie, Goddard, Oberth, and Valier followed the path of Tsiolkovskii, repeating his work and advancing it theoretically (Oberth) and experimentally (Goddard). An essentially new contribution to this difficult problem was made by Tsander."

Tsander was proud of his firsts. Some are important today and some are not. Tsander considered himself the first to consider using components of the launch vehicle as the fuel. Specifically, he wondered why the wings of a spacecraft could not be used as the fuel once above the atmosphere. Or the fuel tank. Reuse of in-space hardware and satellite components is a concept we are just undertaking today. It is known as additive manufacturing, or more commonly, 3D printing. But still, no one is suggesting that one can tear off the launch vehicle and use it as fuel. Interesting thought.

Tsander was one of the first to study using the gravity forces of the Moon and the planets to accelerate and slow down interplanetary missions. This orbital trajectory maneuver has become standard in the space age. It's how NASA's Jet Propulsion Agency and other space agencies' interplanetary missions navigate to their far distant destinations in the solar system. Or using static electricity to deflect asteroids from hitting a rocket, as well as using the sun's rays to power a spaceship. He also analyzed interplanetary flight trajectories to Mars for optimal fuel efficiency and studied using winged spacecraft for re-entry, much like the NASA space shuttle a half century later.

His 1924 *Flights to Other Planets and the Moon* cemented his reputation. Tsander was a Russian combination of Germany's Hermann Oberth and Willy Ley, in that he was both a rocket engineer and a promotor for space travel. Colleagues loved it when Tsander would shout "On to Mars, On to Mars!" whenever a difficult problem had been solved.

Tsander was also a utopian who passionately shared Tsiolkovsky's cosmism optimism that the future of humanity was on planets other than Earth. He was quoted as saying that people living on the Moon "could probably construct a habitation in which living conditions would be much better than on the Earth." The promise of a better life in the stars.

Better than Moscow.
Better than Russia.
Better than Earth.

Fortunately, the Soviet leadership was supportive of his obsession with living among the stars. In 1920, Vladimir Lenin heard Tsander lecture at the Provincial Conference of Inventors in Moscow and asked to speak to the space pioneer.

Vladmir Lenin Supports Friedrich Tsander

But the economic situation in the country was dire, and soon the communist government's modest support for Tsander's research was terminated. But his engine studies were able to continue, as the workers at the Aviation Plant donated 1% of their wages to the rocket designer. Fickleness of government support is well understood today, but factory workers contributing from their salaries to support innovation is incredibly unusual! To state the obvious, Tsander must have been an inspirational engineer and true space travel believer.

VLADIMIR ILYICH LENIN ASKED ME: "WILL YOU BE THE FIRST TO FLY (TO SPACE)?"

I REPLIED THAT I DON'T THINK OTHERWISE, BECAUSE I HAVE TO SET AN EXAMPLE, AND OTHERS WILL BOLDLY FLY AFTER ME.

—*Fredrich Tsander*

CHAPTER 11
The First Encyclopedia of Space
1928

Put everything happening about space exploration together into one collection of books.

This was the challenge of Nikolai Alekseevich Rynin, who decided to assemble into one series all the knowledge worldwide from rocket engineers and mathematicians. It was the world's first encyclopedia on space exploration.

His effort started the same year that the film *Aelita* premiered. The project ended up taking eight long years to fully assemble, with the first volume being published only in 1928.

The finished product was a nine-volume encyclopedia known as *Interplanetary Communications*, which assembled the works of Oberth, Goddard, Tsiolkovsky, Tsander and others, as well as the folk tales and science fiction writings from previous centuries. It is one of the most amazing efforts in the early history of space travel, one done out of pure love.

The idea of interplanetary travel is gradually being taken up by ever-increasing circles of people in various countries, where formal and informal study groups have been established. The American Interplanetary Society has been organized in the USA; in Germany, Der Verein für Raumschiffahrt is operating. In France, Le Comite d'Astronautique has been established, with the tradition of an annual prize award for the best treatise on inter-planetary travel. In the USSR, the Society for the Interplanetary Travel was organized in Moscow back in 1924, but unfortunately it ceased its activities the same year. Numerous study groups among university students were temporarily organized during the years in various towns in the USSR, and especially in Leningrad, but because of the shortage of funds, the complex problems involved, and pressing academic duties, these groups could not show intense activity.

It is clear however that the topic of interplanetary travel is attracting increasing attraction among both scientists and layman in the USSR....an indication of this growing interest is provided by the establishment of "GRID" (Gruppo po Izucheniyu Reaktivnogo Dvizhenyia)

Study Group for Rocket and Propulsion under the auspices of Osoviakhim. (Soviet Society for the Advancement of Civil Defense and Aviation-Chemical industry) in Moscow and Leningrad. Both groups have several hundred registered members.

A considerable volume of new material has accumulated in my files which was not included in earlier issues. It will be included in the next issue, if I am lucky enough to see it through printing.

—Professor Nikolai Rynin

Here's a real important point: Rynin and his fellow contributors, including the science writer Yakov Isidorovich Perelman, wrote to international experts asking for their most recent work. And each responded! How cool is that? Before any governments were involved to shut down international correspondence.

The resulting collection is a kaleidoscope of the musings, the equations and the conclusions of the first generation of rocket mathematicians and constructors, from France, Germany, United States, Austria and Russia. There was no equal to Rynin's encyclopedia in Germany, nor in America. And not until the 1960s was the work translated into English.

Rynin also broke down the technical contributions of many of the rocket pioneers. Readers could see clearly who was focusing on rocket travel to the Moon, to Mars and even to Venus!

It's clear that the first generation of German and Russian pioneering space visionaries were motivated by science fiction writers like the French Jules Verne and the British H.G. Wells. But the next generation, the one that would build the world's first rockets to journey to space, were no doubt mesmerized by Rynin's collected works of the still-living space pioneers.

Some results of rocket flight calculations carried out by the scientists mentioned are compared in Table 14.

TABLE 14

Scientist and year	Tsiolkovskii 1903	Esnault-Pelterie 1913	Goddard 1909		Oberth 1923	Valier 1924		Hohmann 1925
Jet velocity, km/sec	5.7	65.3	3.63	2.134	3.0	4.0	5.7	2.0
Flight acceleration, m/sec^2	100	10.8	45.7	45.7	40	—	100	30
Initial-to-final mass ratio								
Launch from Earth into infinity	9	—	43.5	602	200	—	10	933
Launch from Earth and landing on Moon	9	—	—	—	—	12.1	—	8,250
Takeoff from Earth, circumnavigation of Moon and return to Earth	< 9	—	—	—	200	—	—	933
Launch of Earth satellite	5	—	—	—	—	—	—	—
Launch from Earth for flight to Mars	< 9	—	—	—	—	—	—	875,000
Launch from Earth for flight to Venus	21	—	—	—	—	—	—	54,800
Launch from Earth and travel to another solar system	21	—	—	—	—	43.1	—	—
Takeoff from Earth, circumnavigation of Mars and return to Earth	10,000	—	—	—	—	—	—	—
Takeoff from Earth, descent onto Moon, return to Earth using retro jet thrust	—	1.43	—	—	—	—	—	—

CHAPTER 12
The World's First Space Travel Exhibition
1927

We are learning about a lot of space exploration "firsts," but that's the point. Enthusiasm for rocket travel was bursting out in all directions, from technical to popular culture, like books and movies, so why not organize a world's fair of space exploration?

Done!

In 1927 a Russian organization took it upon themselves to organize what appears to be the world's earliest international exhibition on space travel.

There are some reports the organizers were a little wacky, made up of students and enthusiasts. But hey, they pulled off the first space exhibition. Others say the organizers went on to form the important Soviet Group for the Study of Reactive Motion (GRID), of which both Tsander and Sergei Korolev, the true father of the Russian space program, took part.

No matter who the organizers were, they gave the exhibition the funky name of the "World's First Exhibition of Models of Interplanetary Apparatus, Mechanisms, Instruments, and Historical Materials." (Perhaps it is a little smoother in Russian?)

The exhibition was an astounding success. More than 10,000 people attended in the three-month period from April to June of 1927! Attendees were everyone from factory workers to schoolchildren.

The entrance to the exhibition matched the soaring expectations of the fairgoers. Upon entering, visitors came face to face with a spectacular planetary landscape, complete with an orange-soil planet lush with blue vegetation. From the planet's sky a silver rocket descended. Alongside a crater stood an astronaut in a space suit. Not sure what word was used to describe the spaceman, as the word "cosmonaut" did not enter the Russian vocabulary for another few years.

Let's digress for a moment to learn how the Russian's word for astronaut came into existence. It's an interesting story.

"Cosmonaut" came from the fertile mind of a forgotten space pioneer, a Frenchman from Poland named Ary Sternfeld. Like Oberth, Sternfeld's effort to devote his PhD to space travel was dismissed. For Sternfeld, it was the Sorbonne University in Paris. So that makes at least two prophetic doctorate degrees rejected by academics disbelieving in the validity of rocket travel!

A prolific writer, most of his work appeared in the French Communist

Party's *L'Humanité*. He even corresponded with Tsiolkovsky.

Sternfeld took the polar opposite view of Oberth and many other first-generation space enthusiasts. He felt that there was no market for space travel, therefore no chance for "capitalist" companies to be involved. Concluded Sternfeld: "It will be the socialist society that will master space." In the early 1930s, he toiled away writing his epic work on orbital trajectories and orbital mechanics, calling it *Initiation à la Cosmonautique*. Once the book was completed, Sternfeld so passionately believed in the socialist model of space exploration that he moved with his wife to the Soviet Union and changed his name to Arii Abramovich Shternfel'd.

Once in the Soviet Union, a debate sprung up regarding Sternfeld's use of "cosmonautique," or cosmonaut, to describe a space traveler. Not until the flight of Yuri Gagarin did the Party begin to use the term, with the Soviet media describing Gagarin as the world's first "cosmonaut." In other words, it took two decades for Sternfeld's new word to be embraced by the Russians! Perhaps it took so long because of its linguistic similarity to cosmism, which was a spiritual belief not sanctioned by the Party. It's possible, yes?

●

Let's return to the Space Travel Exhibition.

International in scope, yes, but the exhibition focused on Konstantin Tsiolkovsky, who, visitors were informed, was more important an inventor than Thomas Edison! What a moment for the often-neglected space pioneer. At long last, recognition and respect from the public that cemented his immortality, not in outer space as he longed, but in the unfolding story of his beloved rocket travel.

The exhibition organizers designed an exhibition path that took the public through the history and current status of space travel. Visitors were first shown the imagined worlds of Jules Verne and H. G. Wells and then progressed to the Tsiolkovsky corner, which included a bust of the Russian visionary. Other corners included hardware displays of Germany's Hermann Oberth and Max Valier, America's Robert Goddard and France's Robert Esnault-Pelterie.

●

Rynin provided further details in his Encyclopedia. The booth for Robert Goddard, he wrote, displayed a steel rocket developed in 1919. The first stage was to use alcohol distilled with water. Then, at a certain altitude, liquid hydrogen would be used with an oxygen spray. This stage would fall away, leaving the vehicle to push higher using a smokeless powder, nitrocellulose. Rynin wrote that Goddard would later "turn away from liquid propellants and manned rocket and rely on dry propellants."

Rynin further revealed that the Exhibition also included a model of an electron-propelled spaceship from the Austrian Franz Abdon Ulinski, a space station concept from Hermann Potočnik (Noordung), models of rockets from the French writer Henri de Graffigny and A. Ya. Fedorov's atomic rocket ship. What? Atomic power twenty years before America developed the atom bomb and atomic energy? Apparently, "Fedorov anticipates achieving propulsion of his rocket with the electro-chemical energy resulting from the use of intra-atomic energy."

Ah, that helps.

At times, off in one corner of the exhibition hall was Friedrich Tsander himself!

Tsander had a booth showing off his technological innovations. Grainy photographs show his glider, a hybrid aeroplane and rocket launcher. Looks more like some mutated lobster with a propeller. He may have also exhibited his space-greenhouse, designed to allow space travelers to eat fresh vegetables on their way to Mars, as well as his first spacesuit designs.

This was more than a static exhibition. It was a portal into the new, promised utopian world of rocket travel and outer space colonies.

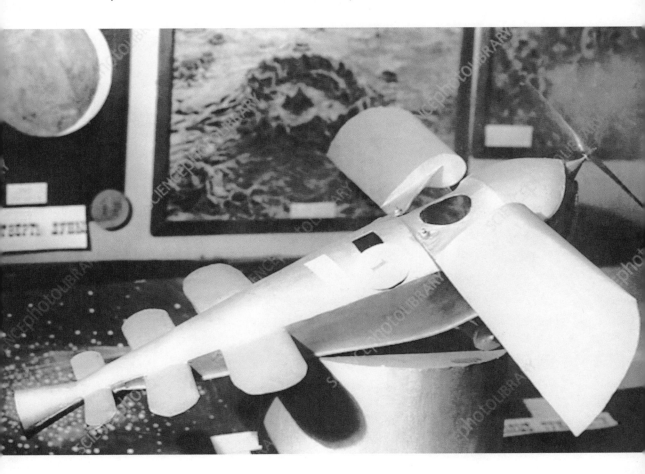

Consider that both Rynin's *Space Encyclopedia* and the Space Exhibition had no parallel in Germany or anywhere else in the world. It was in Russia that there was the collective effort to assemble the world's space pioneers together. There was the pride of having the leading visionary of this new frontier recognized as Russian, and underpinning the enthusiasm was a spiritual belief that did not exist elsewhere. All these contributions made Russia the leader of rocket travel in the 1920s.

SIMILARITIES BETWEEN THE RUSSIAN
AND GERMAN SPACE CRAZE OF THE 1920S

Founding visionaries influenced by Jules Verne write on rocket travel	Yup
Amateur space societies are formed	Yup
Space science fiction films attract huge audiences	Yup
Public enthusiasm reaches a fever pitch	Yup
New players are involved with supporting ideas	Yup
Everyone assumes space travel will be commercial, like aviation	Yup
International correspondence is common	Yup
The governments begin to take notice	Yeah

It must have seemed so inevitable in the late 1920s that soon enough the first rockets would be launched into outer space, followed in a couple of decades by the first astronauts and crewed space stations, and after that the first colonies on the Moon. Companies, as true in aviation, would be created to build and run the vehicles. Customers would include commercial services; like rocket mail for stamp collectors; government services such as using space stations to monitor enemy territory; and partnerships with government and visionaries to create new systems, like space-based solar-powered energy stations.

Everyone could draw inspiration from the vibrant progress in aviation. From the Wright brothers' first flights in 1903 to airplanes being used in the World War to Charles Lindbergh's 1927 solo flight from New York to Paris. Twenty-four years from novelty to government military use, to electrifying the world with personal exploration, to paying passengers using aviation to visit families and take honeymoon trips.

Why not the same for space travel?

Yet, some of the first-generation pioneers suspected that space travel would evolve differently than airplanes or automobiles. Let's meet one of them. And he was neither Russian nor German.

"BEHIND THE GLASS IS FANTASTIC LANDSCAPE OF AN UNKNOWN PLANET, ORANGE SOIL, BLUE VEGATATION....

HAVING MADE ONLY A COUPLE OF STEPS I, AS IT WERE, CROSSED THE THRESHOLD OF ONE ERA TO ANOTHER—THE SPACE AGE."

Mikhail Popov, exhibit organizer

CHAPTER 13
Finally, A True Space Businessperson

The most significant space pragmatist of the 1920s was the Frenchman Robert Esnault-Pelterie.

Yes, I know this episode is focused on Russia. But it's also about putting together all the different people and forces that led to the building of the world's first spaceships. And REP (as he was known) was part of the ecosystem of both the emerging Russian and German space communities and helped evolve the commercial space community forward. So, it's important to include Robert Esnault-Pelterie.

There have been brief mentions of REP in our story, including Rynin's description of the Exhibition of Space Hardware. But his unique contribution is more for being a businessperson who sought to advance space with the proven business model from the aviation industry. Esnault-Pelterie was both successful and not. And how he failed was a sign of the future political direction of space exploration throughout the 20th century.

Before getting involved with the space effort, the Frenchman became enthralled by the new field of aviation and obtained the fourth pilots license in all of France. This was a notable feat which almost killed him when a plane accident forced him to give up piloting forever.

In 1908 he built the world's first monoplane and then somehow obtained a copy of the Wright brothers' plane and set out to create an improved version. (There must be a fascinating story as to how he reengineered the plane!) His family invested in his projects and was almost ruined. But Esnault-Pelterie finally hit the jackpot: he developed and patented the joystick for controlling an airplane. After the World War, he successfully sued airplane manufacturers who had incorporated his device. He also created the four-bladed propeller and a speed indicator, all of which became standard features on early airplanes.

REP found time for his other fascination, that of interplanetary travel. His first work was presented as a lecture, published the following year in a 1913 French journal: *Considération sur les résultats d'un allégement indéfini des moteurs. (Consideration of the results from unlimited lightening of engines.)* Interestingly, one of the first lectures REP gave on the subject of rocket engine propulsion was in Russia.

In his lecture, Esnault-Pelterie showed himself firmly in the camp of practical rocket visionaries, stating how "numerous authors made the study of a man traveling from star to star the subject of fiction. No one has sought to think through the physical requirements...that is the aim of this study." Remember, this was before Oberth's failed dissertation, before Goddard's technical papers and first launch. And REP did not know of Tsiolkovsky.

SOME PREDICTIONS OF ROBERT ESNAULT-PELTERIE:

—Soon rocket flights from Paris to New York would be commonplace, with a journey time of just 24 minutes
—Within 25 years, interplanetary travel would be realized
—Liquid-propellant rocket engines should include cryogenic fuels
—Interplanetary flights could use atomic energy to power the rockets

REP also proposed a human mission to the Moon with a passive thermal control, by having the spaceship have a light side and a dark side that could be rotated to control the temperature during the voyage.

The Frenchman was also among the first to realize that rockets might be useful for more than interplanetary travel. At the dawn of air travel, he was already working the possibilities for what we call today "point to point" supersonic travel between cities.

And REP had one more prediction. And that was that all this vehicle development would cost considerable sums of money, beyond the reach of individuals. Far more expensive than airplanes. That meant the deep pockets of governments would be needed.

While so many were ecstatic over rockets paving the way for living on the Moon, Esnault-Pelterie correctly foresaw the military possibilities. If a rocket could journey to the Moon, he realized, then think of the punch possible if a different trajectory took a rocket launched from Paris not to the Moon but to crash onto, say, London or Moscow or New York. And if the amount of funds needed to develop launch vehicles was far more than that for airplanes, then why not combine the two markets for this powerful new technology and attract the ultimate customer for funds?

In other words, have national governments pay for the development of rockets for their military use and let commercial companies use more economically efficient vehicles for interplanetary passenger travel. A great partnership, right?

Maybe.

And REP was right, wasn't he? Rockets *were* too expensive for commercial entrepreneurs, right? History has shown it took billions of dollars to launch the first humans into space, and hundreds of billions more for the first space stations and missions to the Moon.

But perhaps rockets were so expensive for the first century of space exploration because they *were* built by governments for military purposes. If the first planes were only fighter planes and then you proposed civilian airplanes, people would laugh, pointing out a ticket from New York to Los Angeles would cost a million dollars or something! Right?

No matter, REP saw the government-dominated future of the industry before many of the other European space visionaries. He was right, but where he was wrong was believing, no doubt, that one could have the same sort of partnership that had been seen in the other emerging markets of the early 1900s.

But others feared the same.

Late in his life, Hermann Oberth revealed that he did not share his ideas of space travel with his Romanian king, as he feared the monarch would use the concept of rockets solely for missiles.

Wernher von Braun, on the other hand, had no such moral compunction about being supported by Adolf Hitler for missile development, and the rest is space exploration history.

A path was taken for space exploration that involved huge government investment and total control of the effort. That path is our collective history.

But there were, we must realize, other possible paths that might have allowed for faster, less expensive innovations.

●

Let's move along. Oberth may have been first in 1924 to outline in *Rockets and Interplanetary Travel* a business case for space stations. But Esnault-Pelterie was not struggling to make ends meet like Tsiolkovsky or Goddard or Oberth. REP was a respected member of French industrial circles, with friendships and alliances from a cross section of wealthy French banking and industry leaders. These colleagues were businessmen, and one of their actions was to implement REP's thinking by seeking funding from friends within the French government for missile development. This was done via a secret report in 1928.

Yet another unnoticed milestone in space travel.

A proposal urging the funding of rocket technology not for taking humans to the Moon but to develop an offensive weapon far more powerful than anything in existence. And once developed, this same missile technology could also carry people into outer space.

The proposal was rejected by the French government. Why? The very suggestion was considered as work not becoming of an officer!

Think about it. One wonders how different WWII would have been if France had been the first to develop ballistic missiles...and if the French were the leaders in rocket travel in the 1950s. The first humans in space might well have been French and not the Russians. And would America have spent so heavily on the Apollo program and the race to the Moon if the competitor had been the French and not the Soviets?

Just before seeking the French government funds, Esnault-Pelterie and his backers came together at his mother's house over a Christmas dinner in 1927 as the inaugural members of the "French Astronomical Society." Wanting to push forward the civilian rocket industry, it was decided that the Society would offer an annual prize of 5,000 francs to award the most deserving innovator. Both REP and the banker André-Louis Hirsch contributed their own money for the first 3 years of the prize, thus having it named for them as the REP-Hirsch International Astronautics Prize, or Prix REP-Hirsch. Hirsch was typical of the interesting people in Esnault-Pelterie's orbit. At 19 years old, this soon-to-be banker applied for a patent for a secret long-distance telegraphy technique using infrared radiation.

●

Five thousand francs was good money during those uncertain economic times. Doing some conversion rates of French francs from 1930 into current US dollars or euros, one gets lost in considerations of inflation rates for gold and comparative buying power between nations affected by the economic depression and those that were not. But if one must guess, I'd say it would be worth more than $20,000 today.

REP wanted a new French word to describe the intent of their prize. In attendance at the dinner was the Belgian science fiction writer Joseph Henri Honoré Boex, who wrote under the pseudonym of J.H. Rosny, The Elder. Rosny suggested "astronautics," meaning "navigating among the stars." Esnault-Pelterie liked it and began using the word in both his articles and speeches going forward.

Today "astronautics" is used worldwide, and by now, in fact, it seems worn for our new era of space travel. New chapters of exploration always require new words.

An important goal of the award was to bring together the space innovators from differing countries, so critical after the World War and essential for any emerging commercial industry.

The first winner?

You guessed it! The Romanian-German Hermann Oberth for his expanded book, *Road to Space Travel*. Oberth deserved the award, no doubt. But one wonders if Oberth was the first recipient not only for his influential books and mentoring of German pioneers via the VfR, but also because his experience with *Die Frau Im Mond* had left him penniless. History does not record what Oberth did with his award money. But it's possible, isn't it? That he used some of the funds to clear his name in Berlin with the unpaid vendors.

Oberth, in giving thanks, recognized the theme of international cooperation, writing optimistically in the epilogue of the book that:

> The French Astronomical Society has recognized this book with the REP-Hirsch award....I did not sincerely believe that a German would be awarded such a prize in France...One can see that science and education are capable of bridging national divisions.

The REP-Hirsch award was given every year until 1939 when the onset of WWII put a firm end to the dream of a commercial, cross-national effort to put humanity into space. One that would, as Oberth wrote, "bridge national divisions." The two Frenchmen truly tried to reward international space efforts. One later recipient was the Polish-French-Soviet space engineer Arii Abramovich Shternfel'd, for his work on orbital mechanics. The final award was to the pioneers that were creating at long last one of the first serious American space programs, with the unlikely name of the "Jet Propulsion Laboratory." More on JPL in a future episode.

Robert Esnault-Pelterie was another part of the puzzle coming together to create the exploration of the space frontier: the businessperson. There might have been dozens more businesspeople, companies, banks and investors fueling space travel, just like there are today, had not governments raced to shut down the commercial march to the stars.

CHAPTER 14

Rocket Travel is Hot, Hot, Hot— (But Not in America!)

By the end of the 1920s, building a rocket to carry humans into outer space was no longer viewed as a joke. More and more skeptics now saw space travel as being the next frontier now that air travel was a proven game changer.

Europeans were devouring the latest science fiction books, textbooks, films and popular articles on the exploration of space. In Russia there was the added element of the religious underpinnings of futurists like Fyodorov and Tsiolkovsky. And we see international correspondence between the visionaries was ongoing. Competition was real. A race to be first in space was developing. But in America very little was taking place except for Robert Goddard toiling away, taking key patents on multistage launch vehicles while being subjected to mockery, or perhaps worse, indifference. The action for space travel certainly was in Europe.

Why is that? There is no one reason. But certainly the reaction from so-called experts to Goddard's dry treatise on rocket propulsion must have had a depressing impact on other would-be American space pioneers. The shy scientist was ridiculed for suggesting rockets could push forward in a vacuum, that space travel was technically feasible.

And no one authority may have hindered American's support for space exploration more than the *New York Times*.

At the start of the decade, the newspaper mocked—yes, mocked!—Robert Goddard for his belief that a reactive engine could function in the vacuum of space and propel a rocket forward. An editorial at the start of the decade called out both Goddard and Jules Verne as lacking knowledge of physics by assuming a rocket could push forward in the absence of an atmosphere:

July 13, 1920

His Plan Is Not Original.

That Professor GODDARD, with his "chair" in Clark College and the countenancing of the Smithsonian Institution, does not know the relation of action and reaction, and of the need to have something better than a vacuum against which to react — to say that would be absurd. Of course he only seems to lack the knowledge ladled out daily in high schools...

And, as it happens, JULES VERNE, who also knew a thing or two in assorted sciences and had, besides, a surprising amount of prophetic power, deliberately seemed to make' the same mistake that Professor GODDARD seems to make....

Three churlish comments from the *Times*:

1) His plan was not original. Yeah, everyone up and down the streets of America in the 1920s was building rockets.

2) Note the "chair" in quotes, as if the professor was a fraud.

3) Implying Dr. Goddard had less knowledge than a high school student.

Oh, and let's kick Jules Verne as well.
But what a difference by the end of the decade.

Astronautics

ROBERT ESNAULT PELTERIE offers through the Société Astronomique an annual prize of 5,000 francs for the best essay on what the novelist J.H. ROSNEY, the elder, felicitously call "astronautics" the art of voyaging from star to star. No mere day dreamer, this PELTERIE.

If man can struggle successfully with gravitation hour after hour and fly from place to place on the earth, why may he not hurl himself to the sister planets? Pelterie's Gallic imagination has been aflame with the possibility for over a decade. Fifteen years ago he published in the Journal de Physique the first thoroughgoing mathematical study of interplanetary transportation. He is the father of the present school of astronauts.

Professor Hermann Oberth has written exhaustively on the conditions that must be faced and the energy that must be expanded in escaping from the gravitational clutch of the earth. An Austrian Franz von Hoefft, would first cautiously ascend and discharge an exploratory "registration rocket" of Professor Godard's (sic) well known type before building an interplanetary vessel. And Max Velier (sic) of Munich talks blithely of making 4,000 to 6,000 miles an hour, and to whom a journey around the world is but a pleasant excursion between breakfast and luncheon.

Their highly technical discussions are more exciting than Verne's "from the Earth to the Moon."

Quite the difference by March of 1928. Respect. Enthusiasm. Optimism. The internationalism of the young industry, highlighting French, German and Austrian engineers, as well as the American Goddard. But with one more dig at Jules Verne.

Lindbergh's shocking solo flight to Paris had taken place just half a year before this second *Times* piece was published. Henry Ford was predicting a great year for the auto industry. "Private" phone calls, almost 50 in one day, had recently taken place between Paris and New York. A time of busting all frontiers of time, of place, of travel.

Why not to the Moon?

But too little too late for America, as the negativity at the start of the decade must have played a role in chilling rocket travel enthusiasm and certainly caused Goddard to withdraw even further from the public. Goddard had no Willy Ley, no Nebel, no Scherschevsky, no movie producer or American storyteller pushing his ideas into the public domain. The practical result is that America had no wave of public enthusiasm for space travel and had to import from Europe after WWII. Ugh.

CHAPTER 15

Throwing Shade on Space History

I f a good newspaper makes a mistake, it usually prints a correction and an apology. This happened with the *Izvestia* piece on Hermann Oberth that ignored Konstantin Tsiolkovsky. It also happens that one of the most famous corrections in modern newspaper history concerns Goddard and the *New York Times*.

On July 17, 1969, as the world celebrated the launch of Apollo 11, the *Times* printed a matter-of-fact correction to their 1920 editorial throwing Goddard under the bus. It was printed in an Apollo 11 special supplement below noted science writer Isaac Asimov's article how *Spacecraft, Like Squid, Maneuver by 'Squirts.*

A Correction

Further investigation and experimentation have confirmed the findings of Isaac Newton in the 17th century and it is now definitely established that a rocket can function in a vacuum as well as in an atmosphere. The Times regrets the error.

Congrats to the *Times*, as the correction was deemed incredibly witty and has become part of journalism folklore. But not accurate and very harmful.

Not at all accurate because it implies that their criticism was correct at that time by stating, "further investigation." But it was known to be correct by Oberth, by Tsiolkovsky, by Goddard and others in 1920 when the editorial was printed. Heck, it was known by Isaac Newton in the late 1600s!

And very, very harmful to our understanding of the roots of the US space program.

Why?

Because from Robert Goddard to the NASA Apollo Saturn program is not the strongest direct line.

From Goddard's work to NASA's first space station is not the strongest direct line.

From Goddard to the current generation of American space entrepreneurs is also not the strongest connection, whether technical or cultural.

The *Times* "correction" subtly reinforced the notion to the 1960s readers, and to subsequent generations of space participants and policy makers, that the roots of the Apollo program from the American pioneer Robert Goddard were strong and important enough to be mentioned the day after the historic launch of Apollo 11.

And not from the German space visionaries, later prisoners of war, captured and brought to the United States, who directed much of NASA's extraordinary race to the Moon. And not from the French, Austrian, Russian and other European pioneers of rocket travel, who contributed so much to maturing space exploration for everyone, including the current space ecosystem in the United States.

The truth is that the American government, like the French government, initially ignored their space visionaries. Making the path forward for a pioneer like Dr. Goddard a hurdle both technically and politically.

The same issue of the *New York Times* that printed the "correction" also published an interview with the widow of Robert Goddard from her home in Massachusetts. Mrs. Robert H. Goddard (her first name was not revealed) was asked about her husband's landmark liquid-fueled launch of March 16, 1926.

"No, I can't recall that Bob said anything, except for maybe 'Let's go pick up the pieces.' He was always saying that after an experiment." The space pioneer's widow further dryly remarked that those were not easy days, with townspeople coming to ridicule Dr. Goddard.

The *Times* got it wrong in 1920 and were again wrong in 1969. Their "correction" may well have stifled healthy debate as to why America's victory in the Space Race needed critical support from a cross section of visionaries and engineers from other countries, in addition to the too-small critical mass of homegrown experts.

CHAPTER 16
Storm Clouds

Europeans fell in love with space travel in the 1920s. Nonetheless, warning clouds were popping up by the end of the decade.

Rockets were more complex than airplanes and cars.

Rockets could be used as missiles.

And, with an economic depression cascading from defeated Germany, across Europe, into the post-Revolution Soviet Union and onto the shores of America, who would pay for rocket development? And for what purposes?

Was government funding for military rocket research the answer?

REP's rejected proposal to the French government was not the first effort to obtain government funding for rocket engine development, not for spaceships to the Moon, but for a new generation of weapons: long-range missiles. Italian General G. Arturo Crocco *secured* funding for secret research on solid-rocket fuels and by 1928 had realized the first small missile launches. But nothing impactful came of his efforts.

Nor was Tsander's conversation with Soviet head Vladimir Lenin the first time the revolutionary leader involved himself in launch vehicles.

A few years back, in 1919, a Russian space engineer named Nikolai Ivanovich Tikhomirov was experimenting with powdered fuel rocket engines. The czarist government furnished no support. After the revolution, Tikhomirov went directly to the new Soviet leader Vladimir Lenin. Funding soon materialized to advance powdered rocket engines for military applications. The resulting organization played a role in the Soviets developing their first launch vehicles. It was also the first instance of government funding for military rocket development.

Did the 1920s pioneers assume that like the aviation industry, the government military needs for rockets would help build a commercial space market? One where private sector companies designed and developed the launch vehicles and sold special configurations to the government customers?

Where crews would blast into space on commercial vehicles and governments would fund uncrewed rockets to carry the huge bombs on the horizon?

A virtuous circle with government funding for government needs and entrepreneurs supplying innovation and competition.

Just like all other frontier markets.

This is what the 1920s pioneers of space travel believed.

REP alone among the early pioneers understood just how difficult the political challenge to realize space travel would be. But no one could have predicted how much was accomplished in the 1920s. The tricky pathway from mathematical equations to public support for the **First Rockets** took place in two countries with remarkable similarities. Involved were artists, public relation gurus, wealthy entrepreneurs and dreamers to support the mathematicians and engineers.

The push to the first rockets needed the ecosystem of the 1920s. But also demanded was a new generation of more practical visionaries. As we shall see in the next episodes, three men emerged that changed the course of human space travel history: Wernher von Braun, Sergei Korolev and Qian Xuesen.

The life stories of these three men mirrored the political upheavals of the 20th century. Each tried to realize space travel on their terms. Yet each was disowned or tricked or manipulated by the key national political leaders of the 20th century. It was a unprecedented cat and mouse game.

So, who would construct **The First Rocket**? And how?

And what personal sacrifices would be endured by these new visionaries? Stay Tuned!!

**Episode 3 is about the
Russian Rocket Builders!**

Notes

The origins of space travel have always been a mystery for me. Despite being involved in the community long enough to question America's single-point dependency on the unproven space shuttle, much of the influencing factors have always been murky. I knew of Dr. Robert Goddard and his pioneering efforts on liquid propulsion rockets, but history remembers Goddard as a recluse. And when I worked with my Russian colleagues, they told me of Konstantin Tsiolkovsky. But he was a loner living in a small town hours from Moscow wasn't he? We all knew of Wernher von Braun which only deepened my puzzlement. How did America become so dependent on von Braun and his German team to realize the dream of reaching the Moon?

The questions were deeply personal. As young boys my brother and I promised ourselves that we would be living on Mars by the distant year of 2000. Nope. Not even the Moon. Frustrating.

Several years ago I set out to find the spark that took the dream of space travel from fantasy to reality. The results were surprising, even stunning. I never expected that the magical ingredients included failed graduate students, famous film directors, overlooked visionaries, stubborn optimists, untrustworthy politicians and successful businesspeople. All of whom knew, communicated with, and, in many ways, competed against one another across national boundaries in the 1920s to realize the first rockets.

I decided to share the incredible story from the perspective of one who has been in commercial space for several decades, pushing to make space more like other emerging markets. And soon enough I realized that the historic graphic novel was the perfect medium, squarely in the intersection of the videos so popular today with the nuances of more traditional literature. I reached out to two great artists with differing styles. I was drawn to Shraya Rajbhandary's bold, sweeping illustrations to reveal the power of the first generation of 'rocket travel' supporters. And Jay Mazhar drew the comic strips, the 'pencils' and kindly did the lettering as well. His classic style makes clear the factual nature of the strips.

There is one exception to the accuracy of the strips and the text, and that is the last cartoon, which has all the major rocket pioneers of the 1920s gathered together in a German beer hall. Otherwise, this is a non-fiction book. Okay, a highly opinionated work, but non-fiction nonetheless!

In terms of recent writings, Asif A. Siddiqi has written the most on the space crazes of the 1920s and Frank S. Winter authored a detailed look at the early rocket societies and their influence on driving exploration program. (*Prelude to the Space Age: The Rocket Societies 1924-1940.*) It was also Winter, along with colleague Martin Harwit, who conducted the interview in the 1980s with Hermann Oberth, which is a wonderful portrait of the rocket pioneer looking back—or sometimes refusing to re-examine, his career. There are many more books and articles on the early days of rocket travel, which will be listed on the web site. In the next section is an overview of some of the founding documents for those of you who enjoy, as I do, directly reading the historic books and watching the first (silent) films on space travel. Cool stuff.

Space exploration is too often a business with both eyes on the future. But understanding the past is vital to make sure we avoid the previous stops and starts and make exploration sustainable and impactful for all of us. That is the goal here.

BIBLIOGRAPHY
Further Books and Silent Movies

Graphic Novels

There are two graphic novels focused on space exploration that are absolutely worth reading.

Laika by Nick Abadzis (First Second Books, 2007) beautifully illustrates the story of the Russian dog that in 1957 became the first animal to reach orbit. The scenes depicting Sergei Korolev, the secret Chief Designer who led the Soviet space program during the great Space Race, inspired me to tell the history of rocket travel as a graphic novel.

Moonbound: Apollo 11 and the Dream of Spaceflight (Hill and Wang, 2019) is a wonderfully accurate depiction of not only the historic Apollo mission to the Moon, but also the historical foundation of space travel. Written and illustrated by Jonathan Fetter-Vorm.

Pioneering Books

There is a core collection from the 1920s that can be read in English. These include:

A Method of Reaching Extreme Altitudes by Robert Goddard
The Problem of Space Travel: The Rocket Motor by Hermann Noordung (Herman Potočnik)

The Rocket into Planetary Space by Hermann Oberth

Interplanetary Communications by Nikolai Rynin
Problems of Flight by Jet Propulsion: Interplanetary Flights by F. A. Tsander
Selected Works (or any translated works) by Konstantin Tsiolkovsky
And, of course: *From the Earth to the Moon* by Jules Verne

You can find a collection of these early books on the *From the Earth to Mars* site at www.fromtheearthtomars.com, as well as a bibliography of source materials. And remember, it is okay to ignore the equations! But when you come across thoughts like this: *"Liquid oxygen as well as liquid hydrogen, pumped from their containers and supplied at a definite rate to the narrow beginning of the tube and mixed in small quantities, could give us an excellent combustible material."* (Tsiolkovsky) Stop. Pause. Reflect. Consider and enjoy that sentences like these reflect the basic mechanics of rocket travel being expressed for the very first time.

True for the thoughts and musings of all the other rocket travel pioneers as well.

Popcorn Viewing

The honor of creating the first rocket-travel film seems to belong to the French director Georges Méliès, for his *Le Voyage dans la Lune* (*A Trip to the Moon*), which was filmed in 1902. Today it is best remembered for the cool shot of the rocket hitting the "Man in the Moon's" right eye.

The film is just under 15 minutes in length, so no excuse not to watch. What makes it so interesting is that Méliès used both Jules Verne's long gun rocket launcher and rocket.

Another interesting detail is that the launch of the rocket was done with pomp and ceremony, much like human launches still to this day. Okay, the launch crew looks like circus performers, but nonetheless there is an impressive send-off involving military guards that speaks to the seriousness of space travel that continues in our era.

Himmelskibet (*A Trip to Mars*) was released in 1918. The Danish film is seen as setting the cinematic stage for the later, more influential space travel silent films. Not realistic but worth noting.

The French director Segundo de Chomón's *Le Voyage sur Jupiter* (*A Trip to Jupiter*) should not be overlooked. Released in 1909, it has some very cool scenes of the explorer climbing up a space ladder, past a young woman sitting on the Moon, past Saturn and up to the very impressive battle on Jupiter. Great imagery. Worth watching for the coming together of an immature medium (film) with an immature undertaking (space exploration), fused in a campy style.

The Russian silent film (*The Cosmic Voyage*) was produced by Mosfilm in Moscow, which is still in operation today. It was shot in 1936 and depicts a Soviet space program in turmoil as it attempts the first Moon mission, ten years into their future. The space scenes are realistic—and they should be, as Konstantin Tsiolkovsky was the technical director for the film!

And finally, of course, the two most influential silent films on space travel: *Aelita, Queen of Mars* and *Frau im Mond* (*Woman in the Moon*). *Aelita* (Аэлита) helped propel the Russian space craze, and *Woman in the Moon* was a key influencer for the German space ecosystem of the 1920s.

Missing is any American silent film worth noting. It would be some time before American directors and writers brought space travel to life on the screen.

THERE WAS A TIME... WHEN THE IDEA OF THE POSSIBILITY OF ESTABLISHING THE COMPOSITION OF HEAVENLY BODIES WAS CONSIDERED FOOLHARDY EVEN BY FAMOUS SCIENTISTS AND THINKERS. NOW THIS TIME HAS PASSED... TO PLACE ONE'S FEET ON THE SOIL OF ASTEROIDS, TO LIFT A STONE FROM THE MOON WITH YOUR HAND, TO CONSTRUCT MOVING STATIONS IN ETHER SPACE, TO ORGANIZE INHABITED RINGS AROUND EARTH, MOON AND SUN, TO OBSERVE MARS AT THE DISTANCE OF SEVERAL TENS OF MILES, TO DESCEND TO ITS SATELLITES OR EVEN TO ITS OWN SURFACE—WHAT COULD BE MORE INSANE! IF WE SPEAK ON THE SUBJECT, WE MAY NEVER END."

—Konstantin Tsiokovsky